HOT TOPICS

Hands-on activities ● Investigations ● Model-making ... and much more!

Inventions

ages
5–11
for all primary
years

Peter Riley

C000139703

Author
Peter Riley

Editor
Roanne Charles

Development Editor
Kate Pedlar

Project Editor
Fabia Lewis

Cover and inside illustrations
Laszlo Veres/Beehive Illustration

Photocopiable page illustrations
Colin Elgie

Back cover and inside photography
Peter Rowe

Model-making
Linda Jones.

Polaroid photos
Linda Jones. Except pages 9, 17, 19 (bottom), 65 (bottom), 67, 75 and 76 (bottom).

Series Designer
Helen Taylor

Cover concept/designer
Helen Taylor

Text © 2008 Peter Riley

© 2008 Scholastic Ltd

Designed using Adobe InDesign

Published by Scholastic Ltd
Villiers House
Clarendon Avenue
Leamington Spa
Warwickshire CV32 5PR

www.scholastic.co.uk

Printed by Tien Wah, Singapore.
1 2 3 4 5 6 7 8 9   8 9 0 1 2 3 4 5 6 7

This book is dedicated to the author's granddaughter, Holly Jane.

British Library Cataloguing-in-Publication Data
A catalogue record for this book is available from the British Library.

ISBN 978-0439-94511-0

The rights of Peter Riley to be identified as the author of this work have been asserted by him in accordance with the Copyright, Designs and Patents Act 1988.

Crown copyright material and The National Curriculum is reproduced under the terms of the Click Use Licence.

The publishers gratefully acknowledge:
The photograph on page 8 of late Mesolithic stone tools in modern hafts has been reproduced with the kind permission of the Trustees of the National Museums of Northern Ireland.

All rights reserved. This book is sold subject to the condition that it shall not, by way of trade or otherwise, be lent, hired out or otherwise circulated without the publisher's prior consent in any form of binding or cover other than that in which it is published and without a similar condition, including this condition, being imposed upon the subsequent purchaser.

No part of this publication may be reproduced, stored in a retrieval system, or transmitted, in any form or by any means, electronic, mechanical, photocopying, recording or otherwise, without the prior permission of the publisher. This book remains in copyright, although permission is granted to copy pages where indicated for classroom distribution and use only in the school which has purchased the book, or by the teacher who has purchased the book, and in accordance with the CLA licensing agreement. Photocopying permission is given only for purchasers and not for borrowers of books from any lending service.

Due to the nature of the web, the publisher cannot guarantee the content or links of any of the websites referred to. It is the responsibility of the reader to assess the suitability of websites.

Every effort has been made to trace copyright holders for the works reproduced in this book, and the publishers apologise for any inadvertent omissions.

HOTTOPICS Inventions

Contents

IMAGE © STOCKER, STOCK.XCHNG

Introduction

The *Hot Topics* series explores topics that can be taught across the curriculum. Each book divides its topic into a number of themes which are ordered sequentially to build up a firm foundation of knowledge and provide opportunities for developing a wide range of skills. Each theme provides background information and three lesson plans, for ages 5–7, 7–9 and 9–11. Each lesson plan looks at a different aspect of the theme and varies in complexity from a simple approach with younger children to a more complex approach with older children. There are also photocopiable sheets to support the lessons in each theme.

BACKGROUND INFORMATION

Each theme starts by providing information to support you in teaching the lesson. You may share it with the children as part of your own lesson plan or use it to help answer some of the children's questions as they arise. Information is given about the photocopiable sheets as well as the answers to any questions which have been set. This section also provides a brief overview of all three lessons to help you select content for your own sessions.

The lessons

A detailed structure is provided for lessons aimed at children who are in the 7–9 age range. Less detailed plans, covering the essentials, are given for the lessons aimed at the other two age ranges.

Detailed lesson plans

The detailed lesson plans have the following format:

Objectives

The content of all lesson plans is focused on specific objectives related to the study of inventions.

Subject references

All lesson plans show how they relate to specific curriculum-related objectives. These objectives are based on statements in the National Curriculum for England. They may be used as they are, or regarded as an illustration of the statements that may be addressed and help you to find others which you consider more appropriate for your needs.

Resources and preparation

This section lists everything you will need to deliver the lesson, including any photocopiables provided in this book. Preparation describes anything that needs to be done in advance of the lesson such as obtaining a balloon pump or wooden dowels and so on. As part of the preparation you should consult your school's policies on all practical work so that you can select activities for which you are confident to take responsibility. The ASE publication *Be Safe!* (ISBN 0-863-57324-X) gives useful guidance for conducting safe science activities.

Starter

A starter is only provided in the more detailed lesson plans for ages 7–9. It provides an introduction to the lesson, helping the children to focus on the topic and generate interest.

What to do

This section sets out, point by point, the sequence of activities in the main part of the lesson. It may include activities for you to do, but concentrates mainly on the children's work.

Differentiation

Differentiation is only provided in the more detailed lesson plans for ages 7–9. Suggestions are given for developing strategies for support and extension activities.

Assessment

This section is only provided in the lesson plans for the 7–9 age range. It suggests ways to assess children, either through the product of their work or through looking at how they performed in an activity.

Plenary

This section is only provided in the lesson plans for the 7–9 age range. It shows how children can review their own work and assess their progress in learning about inventions. It is not related to other lessons, but if you are planning a sequence of lessons you may also like to use it to generate interest in future studies of inventions.

Outcomes

These are only provided in the lesson plans for the 7–9 age range and relate to the general objectives. You may wish to add more specific outcomes.

Extension

This section is found in the lesson plans for 5–7 and 9–11 year olds. It allows you to take the initial content of the lesson further.

Flexibility and extra differentiation

As the lessons in each topic are clustered around a particular theme, you may wish to add parts of one lesson to parts of another. For example, in Lesson 2 in Theme 4, on windmills, you may like to add part of Lesson 1 from Theme 1, about using stones to grind corn.

In the lesson plans for 7–9 year olds, differentiation is addressed directly with its own section and, for the other age groups, it is addressed by providing ideas for extension work. The themes, are arranged so that you may also pick activities from the different age groups to provide differentiation. For example, in a lesson for ages 5–7, you may wish to add activities from the lesson for 7–9 year olds in the same theme.

ILLUSTRATION © LASZLO VERES/BEEHIVE ILLUSTRATION

Planning a project

You may like to use the topic for a class or whole school project culminating in an Invention Day. This will need considerable preparation, but the result could be a very memorable event. This section provides some suggestions for activities leading up to the day and a programme of events.

The activities in the tables in this section are based on activities in the lesson plans shown in the third column. Read through each lesson plan to work out how you will use or develop the activity in the context of your Invention Day.

Times are given in the first column for guidance only. Depending on your circumstances, you may wish to lengthen or shorten any of the activities.

Invention Day: ages 5–7
Preparation

● If appropriate, send a letter home asking parents or carers to help make white clothes for the 'inventors'. Alternatively, as most present day inventors work in their own clothes, you could have an 'Own Clothes Day'. If you feel that some children will not be able to bring clothing, collect items that they could wear.

● You may like to have an Invention Day picnic which could be linked to a healthy eating topic. (You should mention this in your letter home.)

● The children need time to reherse the music and dance for 'Tinker toys' (Theme 9 Lesson 1). Their performance could form part of an end-of-day assembly for the whole school.

● During the display period, ask the children whether they have any ideas for a new invention to make life easier.

Ages 5–7		Activity	Lesson plan	Pages
MORNING	60 minutes	Stones and pots	The Stone Age Theme 1 Lessons 1 and 2	9–11/ 13–14
	60 minutes	From sledge to cart	Wheels Theme 3 Lessons 1 and 2	25–27/ 29–30
	30 minutes	The waterwheel	Using energy Theme 4 Lesson 1	33/37
AFTERNOON	20 minutes	A model submarine	Water and air travel Theme 5 Lesson 2	42–43/ 46
	20 minutes	Making a sand timer	Measuring time Theme 6 Lesson 1	49/53
	30 minutes	Making a lighthouse	Using electricity Theme 7 Lesson 1	57/61
	20 minutes	Making a simple telephone	Communication Theme 8 Lesson 1	65/69
	20 minutes	Toys, music and dance	Inventions everywhere Theme 9 Lesson 1	73/77
	20 minutes	Display of inventions made during the day		

IMAGE © SALLADHOR, STOCK.XCHNG

Invention Day: ages 7–9
Preparation

• If appropriate, send a letter home asking parents or carers to help make white clothes for the 'inventors'. Alternatively, as most present day inventors work in their own clothes, you could have an 'Own Clothes Day'. If you feel that some children will not be able to bring clothing, collect items that they could wear.

• You may like to have an Invention Day picnic, which could be linked to a healthy eating topic. (You should mention this in your letter home.)

• You may like to hold an assembly to set the scene. Nine children could use semaphore flags to send a message from the stage, 'Welcome to Invention Day.' Other children could make a poster for each sign, representing the letters in each word, and display these in the school entrance.

• During the display period ask the children if they have any ideas for a new invention to make life easier.

Invention Day: ages 9–11
Preparation

• If appropriate, send a letter home asking parents or carers to help make white clothes for the 'inventors'. As many inventions originated in Victorian times, you could integrate the day with Victorians studies and ask for Victorian costumes to be made. If you feel that some children will not be able to bring white clothes or costumes, you should collect items that they could wear. Alternatively, as most present day inventors work in their own clothes, you could have an 'Own Clothes Day'.

• You may like to have an Invention Day picnic which could be linked to a topic on healthy eating (You should mention this in your letter home.)

• During the display period, ask the children for ideas for a new invention to make life easier.

Ages 7–9		Activity	Lesson plan	Pages
MORNING	40 minutes	Stones and pots	The Stone Age Theme 1 Lessons 1 and 2	9–11/ 13–14
	30 minutes	A simple cart	Wheels Theme 3 Lesson 2	26–27/ 30
	40 minutes	Waterwheel and windmill	Using energy Theme 4 Lessons 1 and 2	33–35/ 37–38
	20 minutes	Make a model submarine	Water and air travel Theme 5 Lesson 2	42–43/ 46
	30 minutes	Make a timer using sand or water	Measuring time Theme 6 Lessons 1 and 2	49–51/ 53–54
AFTERNOON	50 minutes	Burglar-proof box	Using electricity Theme 7 Lesson 2	58–59/ 62
	40 minutes	Sending speedy messages by semaphore	Communication Theme 8 Lesson 2	66–67/ 70
	40 minutes	Wings and jets	Water and air travel Theme 5 Lesson 3*	44/47
	20 minutes	Display of inventions made during the day		

*You could add to this activity with a paper aeroplane design competition.

Ages 9–11		Activity	Lesson plan	Pages
MORNING	40 minutes	Stone Age axe	The Stone Age Theme 1 Lesson 3	12/15
	30 minutes	A simple cart	Wheels Theme 3 Lesson 2	26–27/ 30
	40 minutes	Pulley and winch for loading the cart	Wheels Theme 3 Lesson 3	28/31
	40 minutes	Sending messages by semaphore	Communication Theme 8 Lesson 2	66–67/ 70
AFTERNOON	60 minutes	Burglar-proof box or fans (Give the children a choice)	Using electricity Theme 7 Lessons 2 and 3	58–60/ 62/63
	30 minutes	Sundial	Measuring time Theme 6 Lesson 3	52/55
	30 minutes	Sign language and Braille (Give the children a choice)	Communication Theme 8 Lesson 2	68/71
	20 minutes	Display of inventions made during the day		

The Stone Age

BACKGROUND

The group of living things to which humans belong is called the hominids. The first hominids lived from four and a half to two million years ago. About two million years ago, a hominid developed which used stone tools. The Stone Age is the period in which stone was used for making cutting devices such as axes and knives. It was succeeded by the Bronze Age, which began about six thousand years ago.

The first axes were pieces of stone sharpened to a point. Some people do not consider them to be inventions, merely developments from the observation that a sharp stone is useful. These people would consider a needle to be a good example of a Stone Age invention because it combines the means of making a hole (the point) with the hooking through of a thread (the eye). Generally, however, axes are considered to be inventions. Other Stone Age inventions include the knife, scraper, basket, netting, rope, pottery, pin and needle (made from bone and antlers), stitch (used to join skins), bow and arrow, spear, pick and hoe (made from antler) and reaping hook (like a scythe).

Early Stone Age people were hunter-gatherers, but in time they discovered how to grow crops and farm animals. Stones were used to grind corn. The larger stone, on which the corn grains were placed, was the quern and the smaller stone, which was placed over the corn, was the hand stone. The hand stone was pressed on the grain and rubbed over it. The ground grains were used to make a porridge and bread.

Pottery was invented to hold and store foods. Food could be cooked in fireproof pottery. Axes were used for breaking up bones to release the marrow, and for cutting down trees to clear land for crops.

THE CONTENTS
Lesson 1 (Ages 5–7)
Grinding corn
The children observe grains before and after grinding them on quern stones. They appreciate how hard it was to grind grain.

Lesson 2 (Ages 7–9)
Making a pot
The children use Plasticine® or clay to make a pot. They use a fork to decorate the pot.

Lesson 3 (Ages 10–11)
Making an axe
The children make an axe head from cardboard and a shaft from paper and then tie them together. The fact that this is complicated may lead them to think that Stone Age people were more intelligent than they had assumed.

Notes on photocopiables
Grinding corn (page 13)
Pictures show how the quern is linked to other aspects of Stone Age life – harvesting crops and cooking. There are spaces for drawing the grain before and after grinding or for attaching samples of grain with tape.

Making a pot (page 14)
This shows how to make a simple pot and what tools Stone Age people used to decorate a pot.

Making an axe (page 15)
This page gives instructions for assembling an axe head and shaft.

IMAGE © NATIONAL MUSEUMS NORTHERN IRELAND 2007 COLLECTION ULSTER MUSEUM, BELFAST

Lesson 1 Grinding corn

PHOTOGRAPH © PETER ROWE

AGES 5–7

Objectives
● To make observations on the effect of grinding grain on a quern.
● To know how to use a simple device safely.

Subject references
History
● Learn about the way of life of people in the more distant past in Britain.
(NC: KS1 6b)
Science
● Explore, using sight, and record observations.
(NC: KS1 2f)
Design and technology
● Follow safe procedures for food hygiene.
(NC: KS1 2f)

Resources and preparation
● Make photocopies of page 13. Each child or group will need: a large flat stone (about 12cm x 10cm x 1cm) and a small flat stone (about 8cm x 8cm x 1cm), a magnifying glass, samples of porridge oats in saucers or tin lids, clear sticky tape (optional).

What to do
● Tell the children about the Stone Age as a period of time from two million years ago to about six thousand years ago. Explain that the first Stone Age people hunted animals and gathered fruit, nuts and roots to eat. Later, they began to grow corn, and they invented a way of grinding corn using two stones – a quern stone and a hand stone.
● Issue the photocopiable sheet and discuss the pictures with the children. Show them a quern stones and a hand stone and demonstrate how they were used (perhaps without grain at this stage).
● Tell the children that they are going to make observations on the effect of using the stones. Hand out the magnifying glasses. Issue the porridge oats and let the children observe them closely and

draw them in the first square on the sheet (or stick a few in place with tape).
● Now issue the quern and hand stones and let the children grind a sample of oats. Explain that they should not put a thick layer on the quern stone, as most of the grains will be pushed out to the sides.
● Let the children observe the ground grains and draw them, or secure some with tape, in the second square on the sheet.
● Reflect on grinding corn in Stone Age times. You could point out that there may be bits of grit from the stones mixed with the ground grains. Make sure that the children do not attempt to eat what they have ground up.

Extension
Querns were used at other times in history and are still used in some places today. Tell the children about other Stone Age inventions that we still use today, such as axes and pottery, using the information in the background section on page 8.

Did you know?
The first Stone Age axes were held in the hand, and most had a point at one end.

Lesson 2 Making a pot

Objectives
● To develop skills in following instructions.
● To know how to use materials safely.
● To learn how to express ideas in art.

Subject references
Art and design
● Apply experience of materials, developing their control of tools.
(NC: KS2 2b)
● Design and make an artefact.
(NC: KS2 2c)
● Explore materials and processes used in craft.
(NC: KS2 4b)
● Learn about the roles of craftspeople in different times.
(NC: KS2 4c)

Resources and preparation
● Each child or group will need: a photocopy of page 14, a 30cm ruler, a lump of Plasticine® or self-hardening modelling clay to make a coiled pot with a base of about 5cm diameter, height of 6cm and rim diameter of about 7cm, a plastic or modelling knife (optional), a shell such as a cockle shell, a plastic fork.
● For the Extension, children will need some string.
● You might also want to demonstrate a quern (see Lesson 1).

Starter
● If the children have studied other peoples at periods of history long ago, for example, the Vikings, Romans, Greeks or Egyptians, construct a timeline back into Stone Age times. Alternatively, ask the children to look at their rulers. Say that the ruler represents a simple timeline, with each centimetre representing 1,000 years, and the edge of the ruler (0) representing the present day. Ask the children to move a finger to the 6cm mark, and explain that this represents 6,000 years ago, which was about the end of the Stone Age. Tell the children that the rest of the ruler represents

the Stone Age, but only the last 24,000 years. To represent the whole of the Stone Age you would need to measure out 20m (1m = 100cm or 100,000 years).
● If Key Stage 1 children have done Lesson 1, borrow a quern and demonstrate its use as an invention which is made of stone.
● Refer the children back to their ruler timelines and ask them to move to the 9cm mark. This represents the time when Stone Age people developed pottery. Ask the children to imagine going back there now to make a Stone Age pot.

What to do
● Issue photocopiable page 14 and go through the pot-making process with the children. Discuss the bone tools the Stone-Age people would have used.
● Issue the Plasticine® or modelling clay and let the children make their pots.
● Discuss the techniques of decorating the pot using a shell to make marks, a fork to make parallel lines, and a single outer prong of a fork (and/or the handle if it is quite pointed) to make single lines.
● Let the children make their designs on their pots.

Differentiation

● Children with less manual dexterity may need help rolling out the Plasticine® or clay to the correct thickness and coiling and sticking the sausages together.

● More dexterous children could use another Stone Age technique for decorating the pots. They could coil a piece of string several times around the pot, below the rim, press it into the Plasticine® or clay before it is fully hard and then remove the string, leaving an impression on the surface.

Assessment

The quality of the construction could be assessed, followed by the ideas and skill used in the design on the pot.

Plenary

Set up a table on which the children can display their pots. Tell them about the uses of pots for storage and for cooking. Talk about other Stone Age inventions that we still use today, using the information in the background section on page 8.

Outcomes

● The children can make a pot using a simple Stone Age technique.

● They can think of a design and apply it to the pot.

PHOTOGRAPH © PETER ROWE

ILLUSTRATION © LASZLO VERES/BEEHIVE ILLUSTRATION

HOT TOPICS Inventions

Lesson 3 Making an axe

AGES 9–11

Objectives
● To appreciate that people in the Stone Age were capable of thinking up and carrying out complex tasks.
● To know how to use materials safely.
● To develop skills at following complex instructions.

Subject references
History
● Find out about people from artefacts. (NC: KS2 4a)
Design and technology
● Measure, mark out, cut and shape materials, and assemble and join components and materials accurately. (NC: KS2 2d)

Resources and preparation
● Each child or group will need: photocopies of page 15, pages from a broadsheet newspaper, a piece of corrugated cardboard about 30cm x 18cm, scissors, sticky tape or glue, a strip of cloth about 0.5cm to 1cm wide x 120cm long.
● You will also need: books (or reliable web pages and an interactive whiteboard) showing pictures of Stone Age axes, a shaft and axe head already prepared. Go through the stages of tying the axe head to the shaft so that you can demonstrate it to the children in the lesson and show teaching assistants before the lesson.
● You might also want to demonstrate a quern (see Lesson 1).

What to do
● If children in Key Stage 1 have completed Lesson 1, borrow a quern and demonstrate its use as an invention made of stone. Tell the children about Stone Age people sometimes being perceived as unintelligent, then show them some pictures of Stone-Age axes. Point out that the stones are smoothly shaped and the axe head has had a hole bored in it, which suggests that it was fitted to a shaft and that the axe head was probably held in place with long strips of leather.

● Tell the children that they are going to make a model axe, and hand out photocopies of page 15. Talk the children through the construction and assembly of the shaft and the axe head. The shaft is made from a rolled-up piece of newspaper which tapers to about 2cm diameter at one end. The axe head is made by drawing four similar shapes on cardboard, of the dimensions shown on the sheet, making a hole in each one then sticking them together and pushing them on to the tapered end of the shaft.
● Distribute the paper, cardboard, scissors and adhesive and let the children make the axe heads and shafts.
● Stop the children to show them how to tie on the axe head with the cloth. Refer to the stages shown on the sheet.
● Let the children tie their axe heads. They may need adult help for this stage.

Extension
● Consider that we often think of the tools and equipment we use today as being recently invented, but point out some from Stone Age times, using the information in the background section on page 8.
● Children could also browse the following museum website and look at many kinds of ancient inventions: www.smith.edu/hsc/museum/ancient_inventions/hsclist.htm.

PHOTOGRAPH © PETER ROWE

Grinding corn

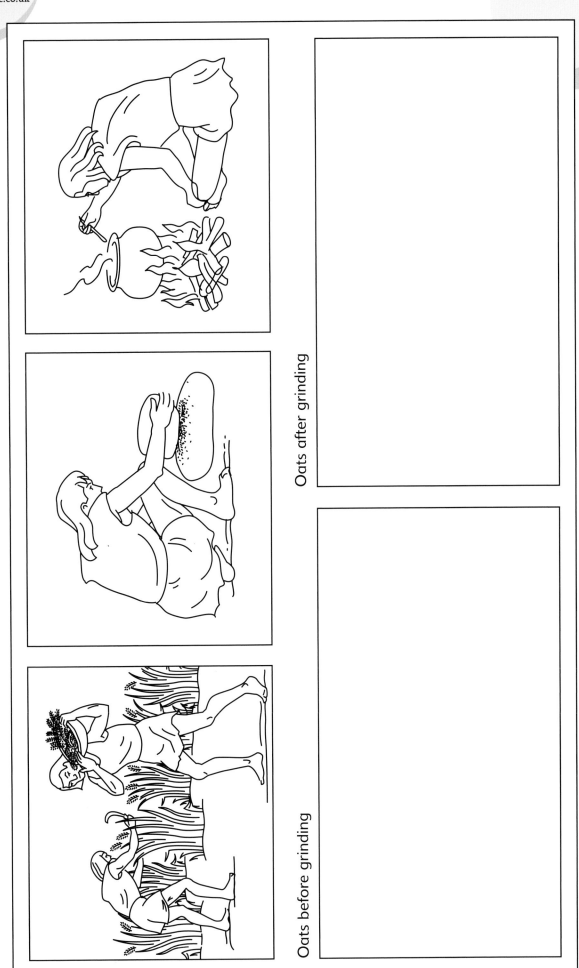

Oats after grinding

Oats before grinding

SCHOLASTIC
www.scholastic.co.uk

Making a pot

1. Roll out a long sausage of clay.

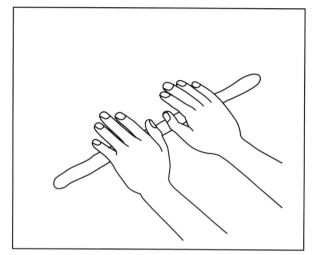

2. Coil the sausage to make the base.

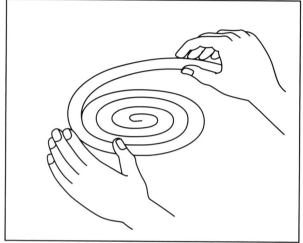

3. Roll out more sausages.

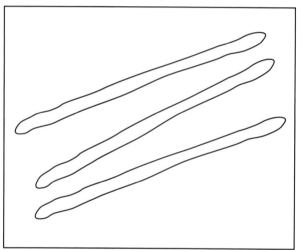

4. Build up the sides of the pot.

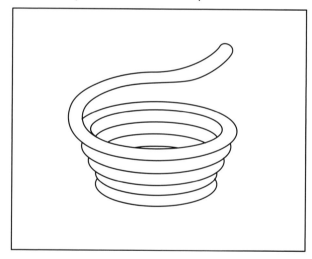

5. Smooth the outside of the pot with your fingers or a knife.

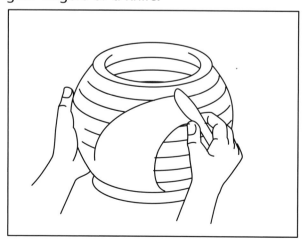

6. Mark with a shell, a plastic fork (antler comb) or one fork prong (bone awl).

Making an axe

Make an axe

1. Roll paper to make the "wooden shaft"	2. Cut out 4 axe shapes.	3. Stick shapes together to make the "stone" axe head.	4. Push the axe head on to the shaft.
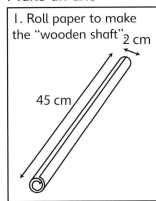 2 cm 45 cm	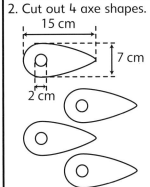 15 cm 7 cm 2 cm		

Tying the axe head onto the shaft

1. Place a 120cm long strip over the axe head.	2d) up and over.	3d) up and over.	5. Once more around for b.
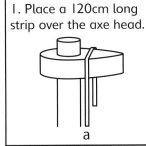 a	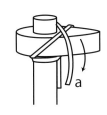 a	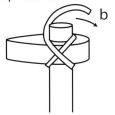 b	 b
2. Wrap the side facing you: a) around the back	3. Now bring the other side: a) around the front	Top view	6. Tie the ends of a and b together in a double knot.
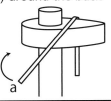 a	 b	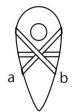 a b	
2b) around the front	3b) around the back	4. Once more around for a.	
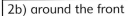 a	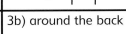 b	 a	
2c) around the back again	3c) around the front again		
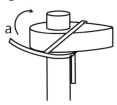 a	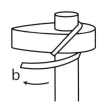 b		

Simple machines

BACKGROUND

A machine is something that makes work easier. There are two forces to consider with every machine: the load force (which has to be overcome if work is to be done) and the effort force (which overcomes the load force and allows work to be done).

One of the simplest machines is the ramp or inclined plane. Think about climbing a hill. Your body is the load, and the distance to the top is the work to be done. If you climb straight up, you will exert a great deal of effort. Going straight up uses a large effort over a short distance. Going up in a zigzag (a ramp) uses a smaller effort, but you have to travel a longer distance. A machine can reduce the effort needed for work by increasing the distance over which the effort is applied.

A screw is an inclined plane wrapped around a cylinder. It allows a small turning force, the effort to move the thread, a long way, around and around to generate a large driving force (instead of overcoming a load), which drives the screw in. A wedge can also be moved a long distance by a small effort, and as it does so, generates a force which can cut through a material. Wedges are found in knives, axes, ploughs and zips.

A lever can be thought of as a rod or bar which has a pivot or fulcrum. Effort is applied to part of the lever to overcome a force generated by a load.

There are three types of lever. The first is a simple see-saw (a pair of scissors or pliers are double first-class levers). A second-class lever has the load between the effort and the pivot (such as a wheelbarrow). A third-class lever has the effort between the load and the pivot (such as someone's lower arm).

THE CONTENTS
Lesson 1 (Ages 5–7)
Ramps
The children learn that a ramp lets a load be lifted with a smaller effort than lifting it directly upwards.

Lesson 2 (Ages 7–9)
Ramps, screws and wedges
The children learn that a ramp lets a load be lifted by a smaller effort than lifting it directly upwards. They learn that a screw is a coiled incline plane and that a wedge is formed by two inclined planes.

Lesson 3 (Ages 9–11)
Levers
The children explore the relationship between the size of the load, the length of the load arm and the movement of the effort to lift the load.

Notes on photocopiables
Ramps (page 21)
The sheet shows a ramp in use and how to set up three experiments.

Ramps, screws and wedges (page 22)
The sheet is in three sections. Section A shows a ramp to stimulate children to design one and then carry out an experiment on it. Section B is to be cut out and coiled around a pen or pencil to show the relationship between an inclined plane and a screw. Section C shows how to make two wedges from strips of cardboard and how to test them.

Levers (page 23)
The sheet shows how to assemble and test a simple lever.

IMAGE © NEYO. STOCK.XCHNG

Lesson 1 Ramps

ILLUSTRATION © LASZLO VERES/BEEHIVE ILLUSTRATION

AGES 5–7

Objectives
● To understand that some machines are very simple.
● To understand that a machine makes work easier to do by reducing effort.

Subject references
Science
● Follow simple instructions to control risks.
(NC: KS1 2e)
● Make and record observations.
(NC: KS1 2f)
● Make simple comparisons and identify simple patterns.
(NC: KS1 2h)

Resources and preparation
● Each child or group will need: photocopies of page 21, two wooden blocks, a long ramp and a short ramp, an elastic band with a loop of string attached to it, sticky tape, scissors, eye protection. (Make sure the elastic band is not too big, otherwise it may not become taut during the experiments.)

What to do
● Ask the children to name some machines and tell you what they do. Through discussion conclude that machines make work easier.
● Issue page 21 and let the children look at the picture of the pyramid being built. Ask the children to identify the biggest machine in the picture and eventually direct them to the ramp.
● Ask the children how the Egyptians might have been able to build the pyramids if someone had not invented the ramp. Conclude that they would have had to lift one stone on top of another.
● Ask the children what they think the word 'effort' means, and look for an answer about 'something we do when we are working'. Tell the children that you can use an elastic band to see how much effort you are making to move blocks of wood: the

more effort you have to make, the more the elastic band stretches.
● Explain the diagram for the first experiment on the sheet, then let the children stick the string to the wooden block. Check they have done this securely, then let them lift the block on to a second block. Ask them to try this three times, then draw the stretched elastic band in the space on the sheet.
● Let the children try experiments 2 and 3 and draw their observations of the stretched elastic bands.
● Review the children's observations and conclude that lifting the block straight up produces the greatest stretch on the elastic band and shows that the most effort is used, while moving the block up the long ramp uses the least effort.

Extension
Ask the children to think of examples of everyday uses of ramps. They should think of ramps at the edge of the pavement to help prams and wheelchairs move over the kerb, they may think of ramps outside shops, or at bus stops, in shopping centres, skate parks and multi-storey car parks. Some drives slope up or down to garages next to houses.

Ramps, screws and wedges

AGES 7–9

Objectives
● To understand that some machines are very simple.
● To construct a simple machine using their own ideas.
● To understand that a machine makes work easier to do by reducing effort.
● To design an experiment to make comparisons.

Subject references
Science
● Know that it is important to test ideas using evidence from observation.
(NC: KS2 Sc1 1b)
● Use simple equipment and materials appropriately.
(NC: KS2 Sc1 2e)
● Check observations by repeating them where appropriate.
(NC: KS2 Sc1 2g)
● Make observations and identify simple patterns in their own observations.
(NC: KS2 Sc1 2i)
● Learn about friction as a force that may prevent objects from starting to move.
(NC: KS2 Sc4 2c)
● Learn how to measure forces and identify the direction in which they act.
(NC: KS2 Sc4 2e)
Design and technology
● Generate ideas for products.
(NC: KS2 1a)
● Plan what they have to do.
(NC: KS2 1c)

Resources and preparation
● Each child or group will need: photocopies of page 22, scissors, sticky paper, ruler, pen or pencil, pieces of glossy card (that slip easily through flour), a thin stick (such as a long match with the head removed), beaker of flour, a small weight such as 30g (but do not issue it until the children have offered ideas for the experiment at the end of section C).
● You will need a selection of materials for making a ramp, to include: pieces of card, wood, books and wooden blocks, a force meter attached to a weight, a hammer, a screwdriver, a block of wood, a nail and a screw of similar length; a model Stone Age axe from Theme 1.
● Rehearse the screwing in of the screw and the hammering in of the nail. Make examples of the wedges to show the children before they start section C.

Starter
● Issue the photocopiable sheet and focus on section A. Say that the main part of the picture represents a very simple machine called a ramp or inclined plane. Tell the children that when we do physical work, such as lifting something, scientists can

identify two forces. One is the load force, which we have to overcome to move the object, and the other is the effort force, which we use to move the object. Lift the weight with the force meter and say that the effort force used to raise the weight is being measured by the force meter. Invite a child to read the measurement.
● Show the children the collection of materials and ask them to look at them, think what they would use to make a ramp, and make a drawing of the ramp (perhaps on the back of the photocopiable sheet).
● Discuss the drawings and select one to build. Then pull the weight up it and ask another child to measure the effort force used. The children should see that a smaller force is used to raise the weight this time.

What to do
● Tell the children to cut the triangle in section B out of paper, place the line X–Y along the length of the pencil and wrap the shape around. They should see that the inclined plane forms a pattern around the pencil like a screw thread.
● Tell the children that a screw is also a machine and can be used to join two pieces of hard material. In this machine, a small

IMAGE © MARXUS, STOCK.XCHNG

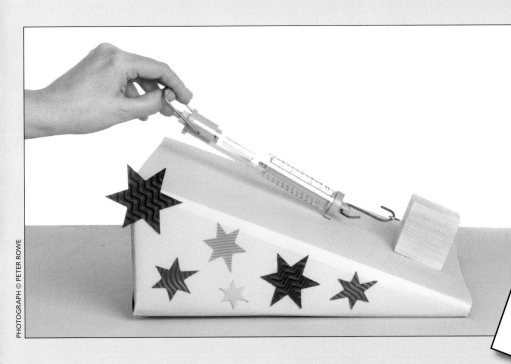

PHOTOGRAPH © PETER ROWE

effort force is used to generate a large force, which drives its way into the material.
● Show how the screw firmly grips the wood by turning a screw a few times into a piece of wood. Now take a nail and hammer that in about the same distance. Let the children notice how much more effort you have to make.
● Pull on the nail and the screw and see that the nail comes out and the screw stays in place. This is due to friction between the inclined plane and the wood.
● If the children have done Lesson 3 in Theme 1, show them a model of a Stone-Age axe. Tell them that the axe head is a wedge, which is actually two inclined planes joined together. Show how to cut from cardboard the two wedges on the sheet.
● Ask the children to make the wedges out of card and mark the stick at 5mm intervals.
● Let the children place each wedge in turn on the surface of the flour and give it a gentle push. Tell them to compare the depth to which each wedge sinks.
● Now ask them to design an experiment for a more accurate comparison. They should think of putting a card across the top of the wedge and putting a weight on it. They should try this three times with each wedge.

Differentiation
● Less dexterous learners may need help in selecting materials for the ramp, assembling the wedge and designing the experiment.
● More confident learners should think about where they have seen ramps in use (see the Extension to Lesson 1).

Assessment
The children can be assessed on how well they make a screw thread on a pencil, make the wedges and carry out the experiment and record the results.

Plenary
● Tell the children that they have looked at three very simple machines that were invented a long time ago and are still in use today.
● Ask the more confident children to report on the everyday use of ramps.
● Ask the class where they have seen screws in use.
● Remind the children that the wedge is used in cutting devices and ask them to think of some, such as a chisel and a knife. Ask them to find the wedge in a zip.

Outcomes
● The children learn that some inventions are very simple machines.
● They learn that a machine helps to reduce the effort to do work.
● They use their imaginations to construct a ramp and design an experiment.

Did you know?
A knife is a wedge that you press into your food in order to cut it.

Lesson 3 Levers

AGES 9–11

Objectives
● To discover a relationship between the forces on a lever.
● To make measurements.
● To produce line graphs.

Subject references
Science
● Check observations and measurements by repeating them.
(NC: KS2 Sc1 2g)
● Make comparisons in their own measurements.
(NC: KS2 Sc1 2i)
● Use measurements to draw conclusions.
(NC: KS2 Sc1 2j)
Maths
● Represent and interpret discrete data using line graphs and ICT where appropriate.
(NC: KS2 Ma4 2c)

Resources and preparation
● Each child or group will need: photocopies of page 23, two rulers (one wooden), a pen, a piece of Plasticine®, eight 2p coins or their equivalent.

What to do
● Distribute the photocopiable sheets and equipment, and let the children set up the lever as follows:
1) Form a Plasticine® block 1cm x 1cm x 3cm to raise and secure the pen above the surface of the table.
2) Make a thin, high wall of Plasticine® at the right-hand end of the wooden ruler to hold the pile of coins (the load) that will develop, and a low wall of Plasticine® to hold a single coin at the other end of the ruler, as the lever raises the load. Try to use the same mass of Plasticine® for both walls.
3) Add one coin to each end of the ruler and adjust the ruler until it brings down the coin on the left, and raises the coin on the right. Measure distance X, and then raise the coin on the right, to its full height (distance Y) and measure it (see page 23).
4) Add a second coin to the one on the right, adjust the lever again until the load is raised and take a second set of measurements.

● The children should add coins, make adjustments and take measurements until there are seven coins piled up on the right.

● They should then produce line graphs from their data and conclude that, the larger the load, the nearer it must be to the pivot in order to be lifted and the greater the distance the effort must move to lift it.

Extension
Tell the children that there are three types of levers, as illustrated at the bottom of the photocopiable sheet. You could say that using a screwdriver to prise open a tin lid is an example of the first type of lever and that a pair of scissors is an example of two first-class levers working together. If the children have studied wedges (Lesson 2), you could also mention that the scissors have wedges to do the cutting.

The children could examine or make a wheelbarrow and examine the position of the pivot load and effort. They could pick up a weight and examine the fulcrum (at the elbow) and the muscle (biceps) providing the effort in the lower arm.

IMAGE © STOCK.XCHNG

■ SCHOLASTIC
www.scholastic.co.uk

Ramps

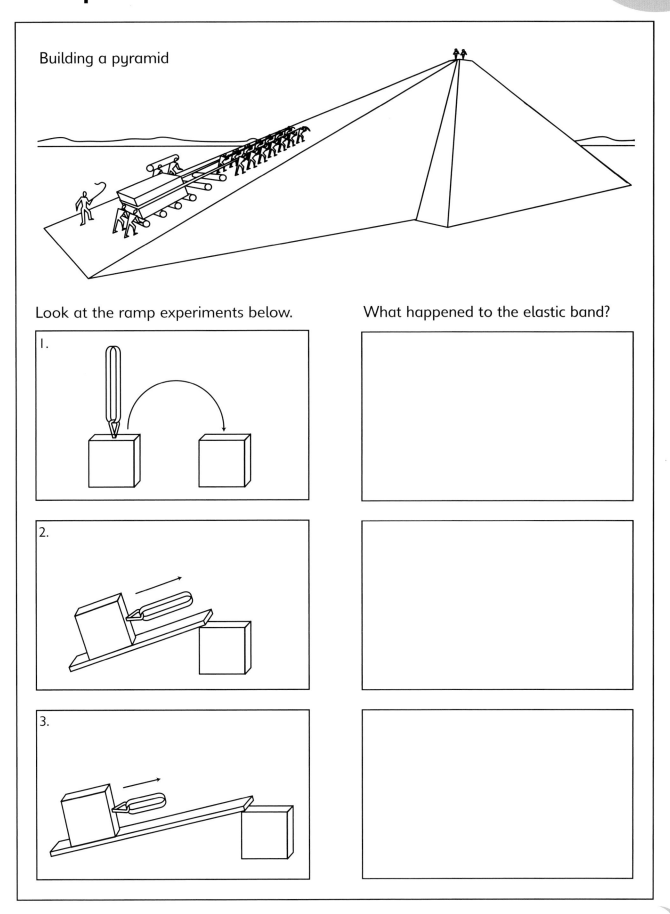

Building a pyramid

Look at the ramp experiments below.

What happened to the elastic band?

1.

2.

3.

HOT TOPICS Inventions

■SCHOLASTIC
www.scholastic.co.uk

Ramps, screws and wedges

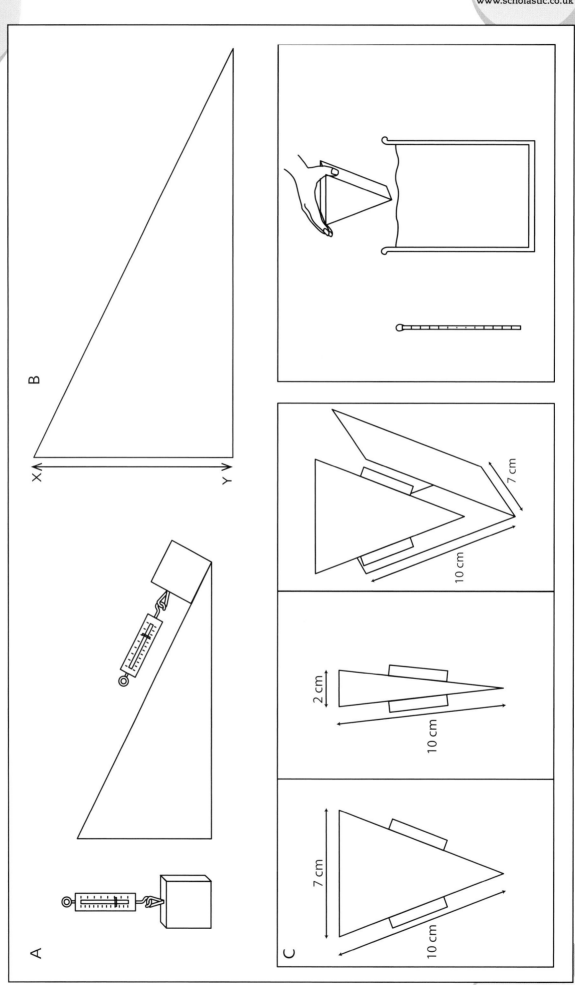

Levers

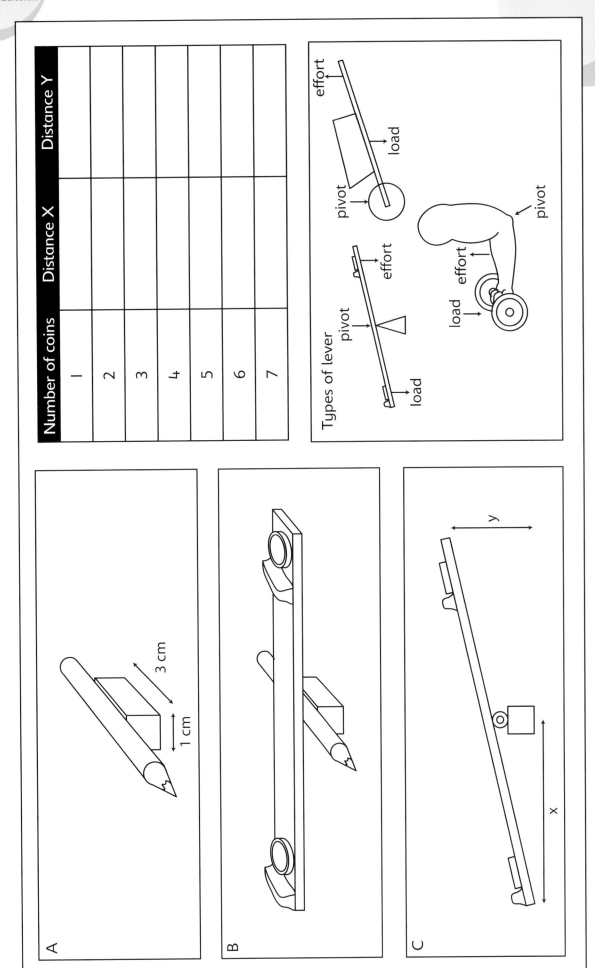

Number of coins	Distance X	Distance Y
1		
2		
3		
4		
5		
6		
7		

Types of lever

effort
load
pivot

pivot
effort

pivot
load
effort

load
effort

pivot
load

A

3 cm
1 cm

B

C

x
y

Wheels

BACKGROUND

The first people carried everything that they needed. In time, they domesticated animals such as donkeys, horses and camels and used them to carry their loads. The sledge was invented to carry loads by dragging them across the ground. Static friction exists between two motionless surfaces that are touching. When you push or pull a stationary object you exert a force greater than the static friction to get it moving. Once it is moving, a smaller force (sliding friction) exists between the surfaces. On a sledge, friction is reduced by having smooth runners.

The wheel was invented not to help carry loads but to help make pottery. The potter's wheel was in use in Mesopotamia by 3500BC. Five hundred years later in Sumer, wheels were being used on carts.

Friction occurs where a wheel touches the ground; this is rolling friction. As with sliding friction, it acts to slow down the wheel, but depends on the surfaces in contact. If the two surfaces are hard and smooth, such as train wheels on rails, the friction is small and the wheels will continue turning for a long time, after the driving force has been removed. If the surfaces are softer, such as a tyre on sand, the rolling friction is larger and the wheel turns for a shorter time, after the driving force has been removed. Rolling friction helps the wheel to catch on the ground and turn. If the driving force turns the wheel too quickly, sliding friction causes the wheel to spin. A pulley helps to lift loads by reducing the amount of friction between the string or rope and the beam over which it passes. A pulley also makes lifting easier because the lifter is pulling down and is assisted by gravity. The first record of a pulley is from about 800BC. The winch is a wheel and lever (the handle), and together they make pulling easier. The first record of a winch is from 500BC.

THE CONTENTS
Lesson 1 (Ages 5–7)
Sledge and rollers

The children make and test a sledge and compare it with dragging a weight on the ground. They try using rollers to move the weight.

Lesson 2 (Ages 7–9)
A simple cart

The children make a cart and discover how it moves, if the axle is not at the centre of the wheel. They invent a cart to carry a pen.

Lesson 3 (Ages 9–11)
Pulley and winch

The children make a pulley tower and test how the pulley lifts an object. They demonstrate how a pulley and winch work together.

Notes on photocopiables
Sledge and rollers (page 29)

The sheet shows a sledge and rollers in use. The stages for making a sledge are given, along with the arrangement for the sledge to pass over rollers.

A simple cart (page 30)

Ideally, photocopy this template on to card, although the cart can be made out of paper. The children may need direction in cutting the tabs and help in making holes for the axles. Wheels are provided on the sheet but dowel rods are needed for the axles.

Pulley and winch (page 31)

This sheet shows the stages in building a pulley tower and winch mechanism and attaching them to a base so that they can work together.

IMAGE © BONVIVANT. STOCK.XCHNG

Lesson 1 Sledge and rollers

Resources and preparation
● Each child or group will need: photocopies of page 29, a wooden block about 11cm x 5cm x 2cm, two strips of corrugated cardboard 0.5–1cm wide x 10cm long, a thin elastic band, sticky tape, a weight with a mass of about 500–530g, eye protection, a dozen crayons or round pencils, space on the carpet.

What to do
● Look at the picture of the sledge and tell the children that the Vikings used this form of transport in snowy conditions over a thousand years ago. Tell the children that they are going to make a sledge and compare it with dragging a load along the ground.
● Give out the materials and go through the stages of constructing the sledge with the children, then let them assemble it.
● Ask the children to turn their sledges upside down (runners on top) on the carpet, put the loads on top and gently pull the elastic bands (A). They should see the bands stretch to about 11 or 12cm and feel that

the load is hard to pull. At this stage it is being held by static friction. When it does start to move, its motion is still opposed by sliding friction.
● Now ask the children to turn over their sledges (so the runners are underneath) and put the load on top. Now the sledge is being used properly and the children should find that the elastic band does not stretch as much as before and the load is a little easier to pull (B).
● Finally, ask the children to put the sledge on rollers and try again (C). They should find that much less effort is needed to keep the sledge moving, but a friend will have to work quickly to move the rollers from the back to the front!

Extension
Ask children to attach an elastic band to a wheeled vehicle with sticky tape, put the load on and pull gently. They should find that it is more convenient to use a wheeled vehicle as there is no need to move rollers about.

AGES 5–7

Objectives
● To assemble a simple vehicle.
● To test the vehicle and compare observations.
● To understand that the sledge and the roller were early inventions in the history of transport.

Subject references
Science
● Collect evidence by making observations. (NC: KS1 Sc1 1)
● Explore, using sight and touch. (NC: KS1 Sc1 2f)
Design and technology
● Assemble, join and combine materials. (NC: KS1 2d)

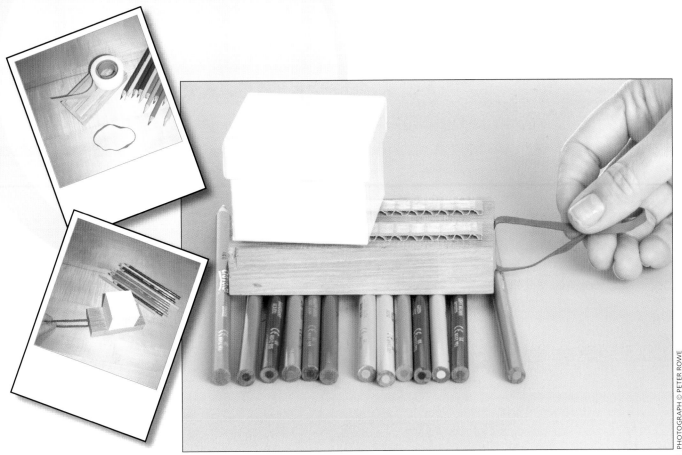

PHOTOGRAPH © PETER ROWE

Lesson 2 A simple cart

AGES 7–9

Objectives
● To assemble a simple a model.
● To think about ways in which the model could be improved.
● To invent a table-top pen carrier.

Subject references
Design and technology
● Generate ideas for products.
(NC: KS2 1a)
● Cut and shape materials and assemble components accurately.
(NC: KS2 2d)
● Reflect on the progress of their work and identify ways in which they could improve their product.
(NC: KS2 3a)
● Carry out tests before making improvements.
(NC: KS2 3b)
Science
● Learn about friction as a force that slows down moving objects.
(NC: KS2 Sc1 2c)

Resources and preparation
● For the starter, you will need the materials from Lesson 1 and photocopiable page 29 to show how they are assembled and used.
● For the main part of the lesson, each child or group will need: a photocopy on card, of page 30, scissors, glue or sticky tape, two pieces of dowel 0.5cm in diameter and 9cm in length, a lump of Plasticine®, extra photocopies on card, of the wheels on page 30.

Starter
Begin by telling the children that in the past, people used the sledge and rollers to move heavy loads. You may like to demonstrate this by making and using the models shown on page 29 and explained in Lesson 1. If the children have been studying friction, you can use this opportunity to show how static and sliding friction differ in strength. Tell the children about the wheel being invented for pottery and then being used for transport. Conclude by saying that friction occurs wherever two surfaces meet and when a wheel begins turning, there is rolling friction between the wheel and the ground which causes the wheel to catch on the ground and help it to grip as it moves.

What to do
● Tell the children that they are going to make a cart, and hand out the photocopies.
● Explain to the children how they should cut out the cart's body, and stress that they should take care when cutting the tabs on the front and back.
● When they have cut out the cart body, you and/or your teaching assistants can make holes in the cart sides for the children.
● Let the children fold and secure the sides then cut out the wheels.
● When the children have cut out the wheels, you and/or your assistants can make holes in them. They should be a little larger than the diameter of the dowel.
● The children then put the dowel axles through the holes in the side of the cart.
● They then plug the holes in the wheels with a small amount of Plasticine® and carefully push the wheels on to the ends of the axles. The Plasticine® should help the ends of the dowels grip the inside of

ILLUSTRATION © LASZLO VERES/BEEHIVE ILLUSTRATION

HOTTOPICS Inventions

PHOTOGRAPH © PETER ROWE

the wheel-holes and also form hubcaps. The ends of the dowel should not stick out through the hole.
- The children can then push their carts and see if the wheels turn smoothly.

Differentiation
- Learners with less manual dexterity may need help folding in the walls of the cart and securing them. They may need help in connecting the dowel to the wheels so that they do not stick out.
- Challenge more confident learners to think how the cart might move if the axles did not go through the centre of the wheel but at some other place along a wheel's diameter. They should take two or four wheels from the extra supply and mark the positions of holes that are not in the centre. When an adult has made the holes for them, the children should change the wheels and see if their predictions are correct.

Assessment
The way the children assemble their carts can be assessed, and also the quality of the end product.

Plenary
- Display the carts and perhaps have a race. The carts with the axles connected asymmetrically to the wheels could be demonstrated. The children could add bodies to their carts which could carry more

materials or have a wedge shape to move faster through the air.
- Alternatively, you could say that as sometimes the children share coloured pencils on a table or borrow one of their friend's pens, you wonder if they could invent a cart to carry a pen or pencil from one person to another. The children could work together or on their own to design carts (possibly long and thin, with a support above the axles to hold the pen without it becoming snagged in the axles), and in a future lesson or in free time make and try to use them.

Outcomes
- The children can assemble a simple model.
- The children can test a simple model.
- The children can make improvements to a model.
- The children can invent a device for everyday use in the classroom.

Did you know?
The wheelbarrow was invented in 300AD in China. It carried goods and people!

Lesson 3 Pulley and winch

AGES 9–11

Objectives
● To use information to assemble machinery that uses wheels to lift loads.
● To invent ways of lifting loads from a cart using the machinery.

Subject references
Design and technology
● Select appropriate tools and techniques for making a product. (NC: KS2 2a)
● Measure, mark out, cut, shape, assemble, join and combine components accurately. (NC: KS2 2d)
● Learn how mechanisms can be used to make things move in different ways. (NC: KS2 4c)
Science
● Learn that objects are pulled downwards because of gravitational attraction. (NC: KS2 Sc4 2b)

Resources and preparation
Each child or group will need: a photocopy of page 31; pieces of thick card about 33cm x 24cm, 6cm x 24cm and 26cm x 35cm; a piece of dowel 0.5cm in diameter and 17cm in length; two cotton reels; a piece of string about 80cm long; a straw that bends at one end; a pipe cleaner; thread; a lump of Plasticine®; sticky tape; scissors.

What to do
● Begin by giving a brief history of the wheel and its applications as a pulley to make lifting easier and a winch to make moving loads easier.
● Go through the photocopiable sheet with the children.
● First they measure the dimensions, make the holes and fold the card along the lines. Then, they thread the dowel through the central hole in the cotton reel. With the cotton reel in place, they then thread each end of the dowel through the holes in the card. A lump of Plasticine®, about 1.5cm in diameter, should be attached to a piece of string and laid over the cotton reel. The free end of the string should be pulled down and the children can feel how hard it is to lift the Plasticine®. If the children now wrap the string around the pulley, they will see that the pulley makes the Plasticine® easier to lift.
● Stages 3 and 4 make the winch support. In stages 5 and 6, the children thread a pipe cleaner into a bendy straw and insert that through the holes and the second cotton reel.

● In stage 7, a small piece of Plasticine® is made into a horseshoe shape, then pressed around the point where the straw leaves the reel. This is repeated at B, and the end of the straw with the pipe cleaner inside it is bent down to make the handle.
● In stage 8, the pulley tower and winch mechanism are secured to a base board. A piece of Plasticine® about 1.5cm in diameter is attached to one end of the string and the other end is tied to the reel. The winch can now be used with the pulley to raise the load.

Extension
Children could make a cart as in Lesson 2, and cut a hole in the tower so that the cart can sit directly under the pulley. They could invent ways of connecting Plasticine® pieces or other loads to the string so that the pulley can lift them off the cart. To complete the wheel theme, they could lower the load on to a piece of card to be moved away on rollers.

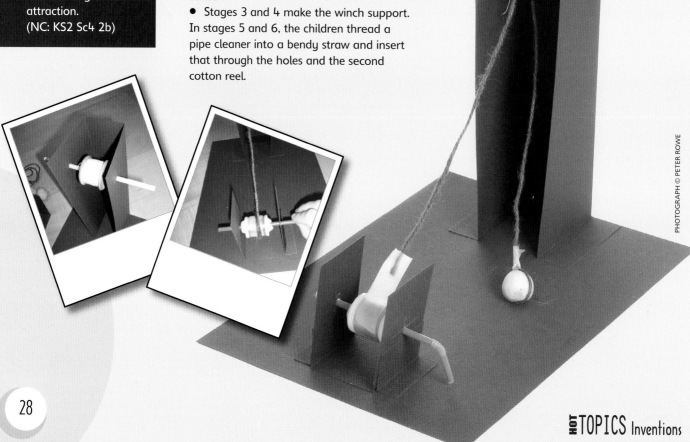

PHOTOGRAPH © PETER ROWE

HOT TOPICS Inventions

Sledge and rollers

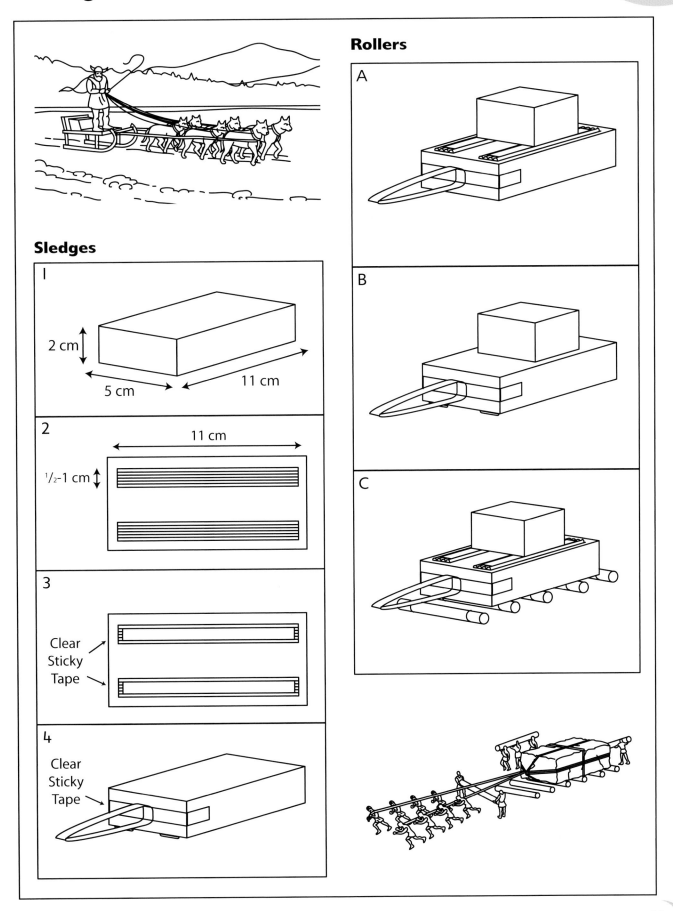

Sledges

1

2 cm

5 cm   11 cm

2

11 cm

½–1 cm

3

Clear Sticky Tape

4

Clear Sticky Tape

Rollers

A

B

C

SCHOLASTIC
www.scholastic.co.uk

A simple cart

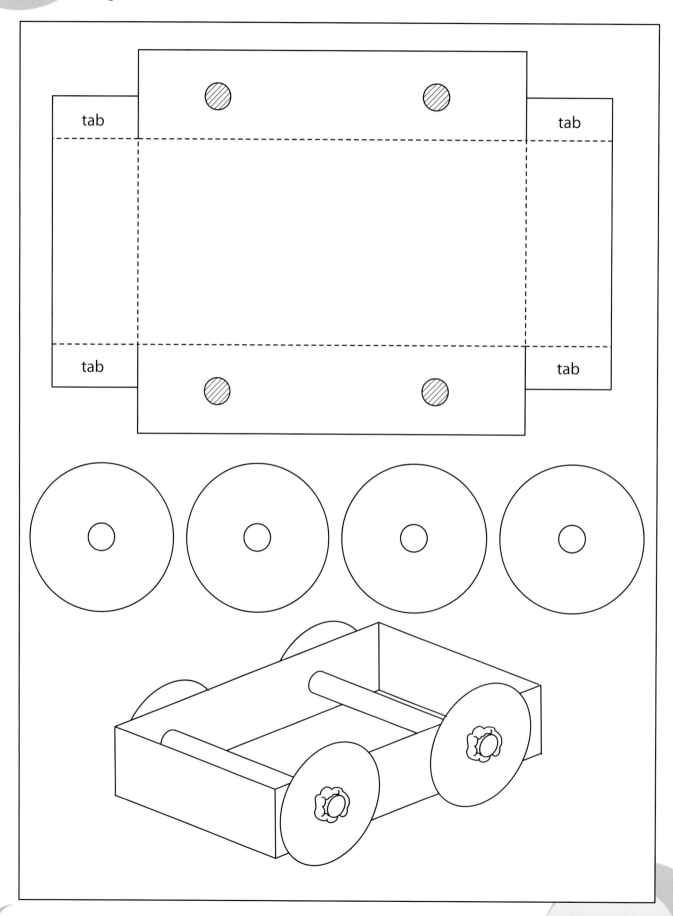

PHOTOCOPIABLE

Pulley and winch

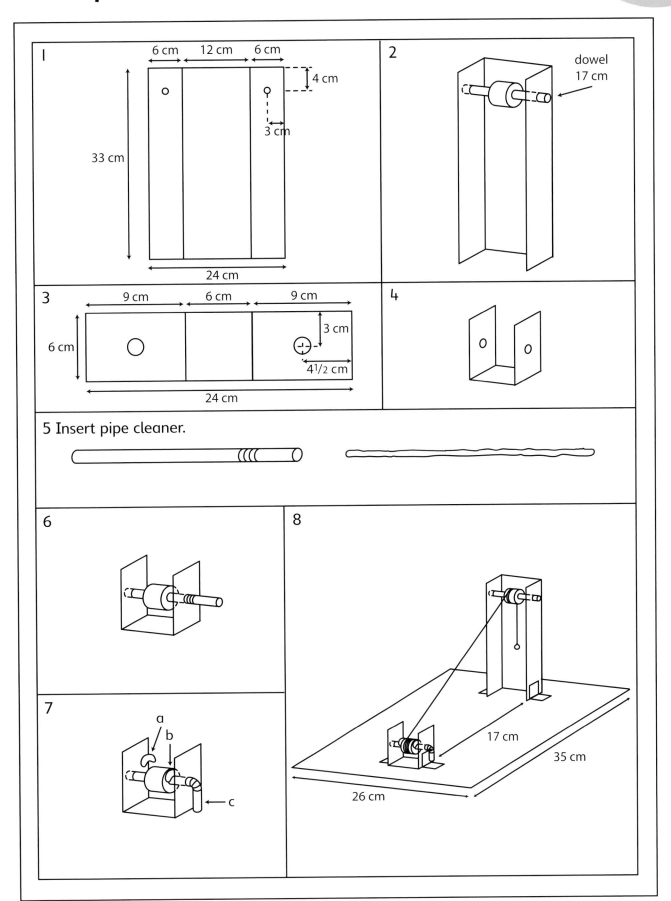

Using energy

BACKGROUND

Energy is needed for work (work is done when a force makes something move). Energy exists in many forms: light and heat, for example, and stored energy, such as that stored in food. Energy can change from one form to another.

Between the fifth and third century BC the first waterwheel was invented, harnessing the gravitational energy stored in water. Early waterwheels had paddles, but by the time of the Roman Empire they had buckets, and this design remained in use into the Industrial Revolution.

The first windmills were used in Iran in the seventh century AD. A windmill uses the kinetic energy in moving air to turn its sails. This energy is generated by the way air behaves when it is heated. It rises, and air is drawn in to replace the column of rising air. This movement of air is called convection. At the Earth's Equator the air is heated most strongly and this sets up a pattern of winds across the Earth. Large masses of air may also gather and become warm or cool, depending on their location. When these air masses meet, they swirl together, forming depressions or cyclones and generating the winds that cause our weather.

When water is heated to 100°C, steam is produced. Steam is not the clouds you see above a boiling kettle, but the colourless gas which escapes from the kettle spout. The clouds of steam are actually water droplets produced when the steam condenses on dust particles in the air. When steam is produced, the volume of the water rapidly expands and pushes on everything around it. In the steam engine, steam drives a piston. In early steam engines the up-and-down movement of the piston could be used for pumping water out of flooded mines. James Watt invented a way of changing the up-and-down movement into turning a wheel. This could then be connected to other machines by belts or gear wheels and led to steam engines being used to power factories, locomotives and ships. The path of energy through a steam engine is from stored energy in the fuel (wood or coal), to moving energy of the steam, to moving energy of the engine components.

THE CONTENTS

Lesson 1 (Ages 5–7)
Waterwheel
The children make two waterwheels and compare their efficiency.

Lesson 2 (Ages 7–9)
Windmill
The children make a model windmill and then consider ways of improving it.

Lesson 3 (Ages 9–11)
Steam engine
The children examine a picture of a steam engine and investigate the action of the piston. They then make a wheel and cam and discover how the up-and-down motion can be converted into turning a wheel.

Notes on photocopiables
Waterwheel (page 37)
Dimensions have not been included to make the waterwheel instructions more accessible.

Windmill (page 38)
The sheet provides the outline of the sail and instructions for construction.

Steam engine (page 39)
This shows a Watts steam engine and a balloon pump, which matches one component of the engine. An outline of a wheel and cam are given, along with pictures of how to assemble the wheel and cam.

IMAGE © J_CASTRO, STOCK.XCHNG

HOT TOPICS Inventions

Lesson 1 Waterwheel

IMAGE © JOLENE00, STOCK.XCHNG

AGES 5–7

Objectives
● To make models by following simple instructions.
● To know how to make a waterwheel perform better.

Subject references
Design and technology
● Shape a material. (NC: KS1 2c)
● Assemble, join and combine materials and components. (NC: KS1 2d)
Science
● Recognise when a test or comparison is unfair. (NC: KS1 Sc1 2d)
● Review their work and explain what they did to others. (NC: KS1 Sc1 2j)

Resources and preparation
● Each child or group will need: a photocopy of page 37, a piece of dowel 24cm x 0.5cm, two pieces of Plasticine® to roll into cylinders 3–3.5cm diameter and 2cm wide, flat clear plastic strips 2cm x 2.5cm, curved clear plastic strips 2cm x 2.5cm (cut from a 1.5l drinks bottle or similar), access to a tap and sink.

What to do
● Tell the children that machines need energy in order to work. If the children have studied Lesson 1 in Theme 1, remind them of how hard it was to grind corn. Tell the children that the waterwheel was invented between 500 and 300 BC and in time was connected to other bits of equipment to make a machine to grind corn.
● Issue the photocopiable and tell the children that they are going to make and compare two waterwheels. Talk them through the stages: A) making the wheels; B) inserting them on the dowel; C) shaping them around the dowel to make them grip yet still keeping their shape; and D) inserting four blades to each wheel (one wheel should have curved blades and one should have flat blades).
● Turn on the tap so that water flows gently. Let the children hold the ends of the dowel very loosely and take turns at holding each one under the tap and observing how fast it spins round. They should find that the waterwheel with curved blades turns faster.
● In stage E, the children add four more blades (between the ones already inserted) and test the wheels in the water again. They should find that the waterwheel with curved blades turns faster and both of these waterwheels turn faster than before.

Extension
● The website for the Ford End Watermill in Ivinghoe, Buckinghamshire shows different kinds of waterwheels: www.for dendwatermill.co.uk/guide.html#6. You could view the illustrations on an interactive whiteboard.
● If you are teaching older children (especially 10 –11 year olds) this lesson, you may like them to investigate the uses of the mills on the River Sheaf in Abbeydale outside Sheffield by visiting this site: www.tilthammer.com/water/sheaf1.html.

Did you know?
Waterwheels called turbines are used today, in some power stations, to generate electricity.

Lesson 2 Windmill

AGES 7–9

Objectives
- To make a model by following instructions.
- To construct a model windmill and test it.
- To evaluate their work and suggest improvements.

Subject references
Design and technology
- Measure, mark out, cut and shape materials and assemble, join and combine components accurately.
(NC: KS2 2a)
- Carry out appropriate tests before making any improvements.
(NC: KS2 3b)
- Do focused practical tasks that develop a range of techniques.
(NC: KS2 5b)

Mathematics
- Measure objects, using simple measuring instruments and scales.
(NC: KS2 4c)

Geography
- Use maps at a range of scales.
(NC KS2 2c)

Resources and preparation
- Each child or group will need: a photocopy of page 38 (ideally, this should be photocopied on to thin card, but it will work with paper), a ruler, scissors, a piece of cardboard at least 24cm long from which to cut a strip, a bead with a hole large enough for a paper fastener, a paper fastener, glue.
- You may like to make a windmill before the lesson and use it perhaps with less confident learners to help them to see what they are making.
- For the starter, collect a large flat stone (about 12cm x 10cm x 1cm) and a small flat stone (about 8cm x 8cm x 1cm), and some porridge oats. These may be available in school already if someone has done Lesson 1 in Theme 1.
- You may like to visit the website www.ukmills.com in order to look at different types of windmills, the structure of windmills and discover the location of the mills around the UK. (The site also shows some waterwheels.)

Starter
- Place some porridge oats on the large flat stone and grind them up with the smaller stone. Tell or remind the children that this was the way people ground up corn to make flour for thousands of years. Explain to them that later on, about 1,300 years ago, a way of using the power of the wind was invented in order to do the grinding job. Ask the children what they think the invention was and look for an answer about windmills.
- Encourage the children to tell you what they know about windmills. They may know something about them from stories they have read or listened to. Alternatively, or additionally, you could display the first website on an interactive whiteboard and look at the many different types of windmill.
- Tell the children that they are going to make a model windmill.

ILLUSTRATION © LASZLO VERES/BEEHIVE ILLUSTRATION

HOT**TOPICS** Inventions

IMAGE © GARY COOK. ALAMY

What to do

- Issue the photocopiable sheet and go through the instructions with the children.
- Let the children make their windmills, but check that they can make holes in the paper and card safely. If not, make holes for them.
- Ask the children to test their windmills by blowing on them or spinning them gently with a finger. Allow them some time to make adjustments if necessary.

Differentiation

- Less dexterous learners may need help in marking out the cuts to be made on the diagonals, and in gathering the sails to the centre.
- More dexterous learners may like to make another windmill, with larger or smaller sails, and compare it with the first one that they have made.

Assessment

The children can be assessed on the way they carry out their practical work and the quality of their finished product.

Plenary

- Let the children show how their windmills work. If it is windy, they could take their windmills outside and see how they perform.
- You could use the website suggested in the resources, to examine how complicated a real windmill is.
- With older children, you may like to search the website to discover where windmills and watermills were built in the locality. The maps show a surprising number of mills.

Outcomes

- The children can follow instructions to make a model.
- They can construct a model that works.

PHOTOGRAPH © PETER ROWE

Lesson 3 Steam engine

AGES 9–11

Objectives
● To understand how a steam engine works.
● To learn about the work of the steam engine in the context of the Industrial Revolution.

Subject references
Design and technology
● Measure and cut materials and join components accurately. (NC: KS2 2d)
History
● Study the changes in work and transport on the lives of people in different sections of society. (NC: KS2 11a)

Resources and preparation
● Each child or group will need: a photocopy of page 39, a sheet of thin card, a strip of corrugated cardboard, scissors, glue, two paper fasteners, access to a balloon pump (balloon not required).
● The website www.keveney.com/watt.html may be useful, as it shows the action of a beam engine, similar to the one on the photocopiable. A second website, www.powerhousemuseum.com/collection/database/?irn=7177 shows a second linkage mechanism on a steam engine. You could also visit www.bbc.co.uk/history/games/beam/beam.shtml to see how steam passes through a steam engine.

What to do
● Ask the children to look at the Watts beam engine on the photocopiable. Point out the main components: the piston which moves due to the steam passing into it; the rod connected to a beam; the beam, which transfers this movement to the other end of the engine; the rod which connects to the linkage on the wheel and the wheel itself.
● Tell the children that the machine can be simplified as picture A shows.
● Pass around a balloon pump and say that it has a piston inside, like the steam chamber in the engine, shown on the left in picture A.
● Tell the children that they are going to make the other end of the engine. They should begin making the rod by measuring and cutting out a piece of corrugated cardboard 16cm long and 1.5cm wide. They need to cut out two 1.5cm squares of the cardboard to make into washers to connect the rod to the linkage and the linkage to the wheel.
● Let the children cut out the wheel (C) and the linkage (D), stick them on to thin cardboard and then cut around the outline and make the holes.
● The children then attach the rod, washer and linkage with a paper fastener as stage 1 shows. Let them glue the second washer to the back of the linkage, as shown in stage 2. They should then join the linkage washer and wheel with the second paper fastener.
● The children can then simulate the action of the end of the right beam (stage 4) with their right hand by moving it up and down, while holding the ends of the paper fastener through the wheel with their other hand. They should make sure that the wheel is directly under their left hand.
● Show the children the first website and let them see the engine working. Visit the second website to examine a second type of linkage. Visit the third website to see how steam passes through an engine and the importance of valves in making the steam move in one direction.

Extension
Some children could look at secondary sources on Victorian mills and factories to investigate how steam engines powered the machines and the growth of the railways.

IMAGE © STEVEKRH19, STOCK.XCHNG

Waterwheel

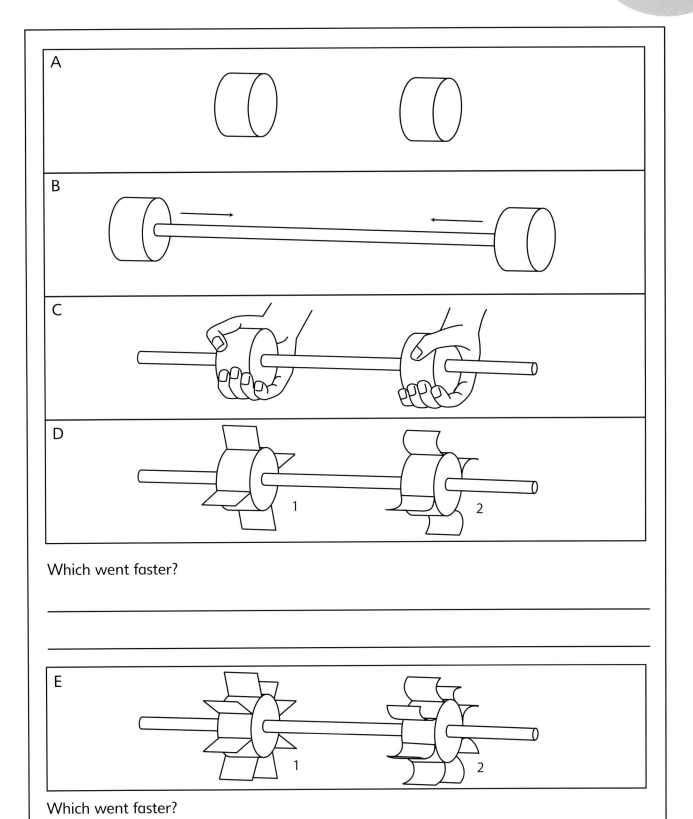

A

B

C

D

Which went faster?

_____

_____

E

Which went faster?

_____

_____

📖 SCHOLASTIC
www.scholastic.co.uk

Windmill

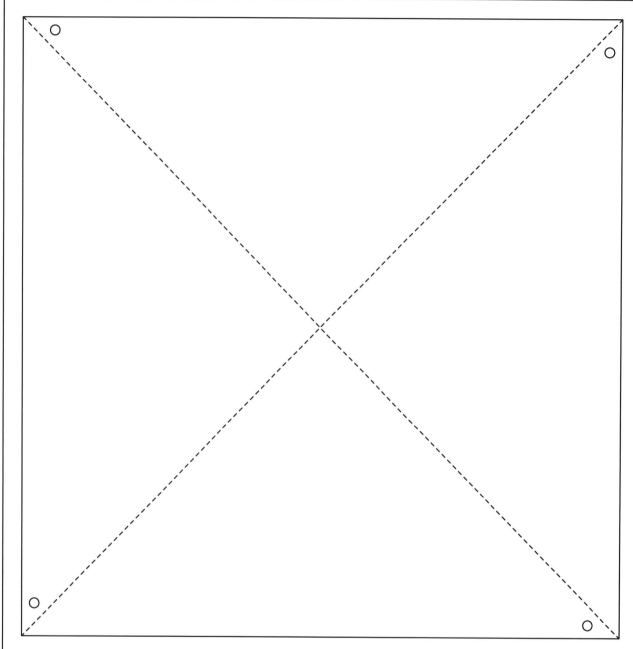

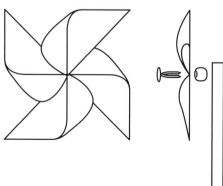

1. Measure 9cm along each diagonal line, from each corner and make a mark.

2. Cut out the square. Cut along each diagonal up to the mark.

3. Fold each corner marked o into the centre and glue it down.

4. Cut a strip of cardboard 24cm x 1.5cm.

5. Push a paper fastener through the sail, a bead and then the cardboard. Open it behind the cardboard to hold the sail in place.

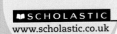
PHOTOCOPIABLE

Steam engine

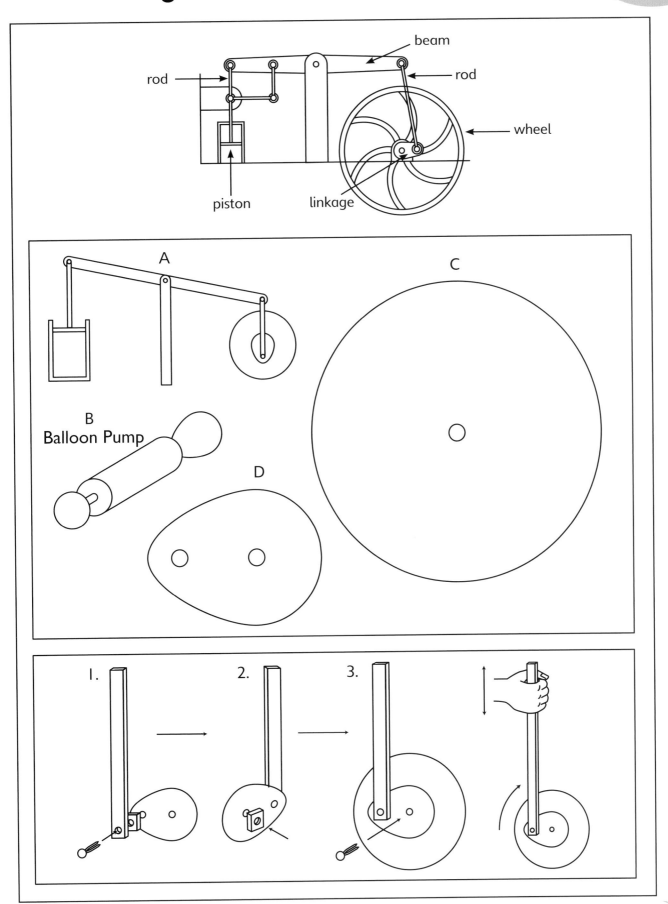

Water and air travel

BACKGROUND

The earliest record of a boat, made from a hollow log, comes from about 8,000 years ago. Another early boat was the coracle, made of a wooden framework and covered with animal skins.

A boat floats when its weight is less than the upthrust of the water. The downward force of an object in water is its weight, and the upward force of the water is the upthrust. When placed in water an object pushes away a volume of water. This volume of displaced water pushes back on the object with a force equal to the displaced water's weight. This force is the upthrust.

The first submarine was invented by Cornelius Drebbel in 1620. A submarine has ballast tanks, which can be filled with either air or water. When the submarine submerges, water is allowed into the ballast tanks. When the submarine rises, compressed air is pumped into the tanks to push the water out.

Two aspects of aircraft are considered in this theme – the aerofoil shape of the wing and the pushing of a gas on the air that occurs in a jet engine. A cross-section of an aircraft wing has a curved upper surface and a flatter lower one. When air passes over the surfaces, the air on the upper surface has a greater distance to travel than the air on the under surface. Therefore, in order for the air on the upper surface to reach the back of the wing, at the same time as the air on the lower surface, it must travel fast and as a result press with less force on the upper surface. The air on the lower surface pressing upwards more strongly makes the wing and aircraft lift. The lift force is stronger than the weight of the aircraft. The jet engine shoots a volume of gas out of its back. The force of this rushing gas is balanced by a force that pushes the engine in the opposite direction. It is not the volume of escaping gas pushing on the air around it that pushes the engine forwards. Frank Whittle and Hans von Ohain both invented jet engines in the late 1930s, but were unaware of each other's work.

THE CONTENTS

Lesson 1 (Ages 5–7)
A dugout and a coracle
The children make a model dugout canoe and test it in water. They then make a coracle.

Lesson 2 (Ages 7–9)
Submarine
The children assemble a model submarine and make it sink and rise in water.

Lesson 3 (Ages 9–11)
A wing and a jet
The children make a model wing with an aerofoil shape and discover how moving air makes it rise. They make a balloon into a jet and launch it in a line across the room.

Notes on photocopiables
A dugout and a coracle (page 45)
The pictures show how a real dugout is made and how a coracle is piloted. The making of a Plasticine® dugout is shown and how to convert it into a coracle.

Submarine (page 46)
The sheet shows the stages in assembling and testing a model submarine.

A wing and a jet (page 47)
Instructions for assembling and testing of the model wing and balloon jet are provided.

IMAGE © MPILKENTON, STOCK.XCHNG

HOT TOPICS Inventions

Lesson 1 A dugout and a coracle

ILLUSTRATION © LASZLO VERES/BEEHIVE ILLUSTRATION

AGES 5–7

Objectives
● To use materials and equipment safely.
● To make simple models that float.

Subject references
Science
● Learn that pushes and pulls are forces.
(NC: KS1 Sc4 2b)
History
● Find out about the past from a range of sources.
(NC: KS1 4a)

Resources and preparation
● Each child or group will need: a photocopy of page 45, a 'log' of Plasticine® 9 or 10cm long with a diameter of about 2.5cm, a plastic knife, a metal spoon, a bowl of water.

What to do
● Look at the first picture on the sheet with the children and ask them what the men are doing and if they think the work would be hard. Tell the children that they are going to make a model dugout, but instead of using an axe and a log, they are going to use a plastic knife and some Plasticine®.
● Issue the logs and the knives and show the children how to dig out a little at a time with the knife blade. If the children's approach is too vigorous, the knife may snap. If you think this is likely, substitute a metal spoon for the knife.
● When the children think they have hollowed out enough Plasticine®, let them test their dugouts. The chances are they will sink and more hollowing out will have to be done! The important point is for the children to realise that this invention involved a lot of hard work.
● When you feel that the children have spent enough time on their dugouts, draw their attention to the second picture and talk about the coracle. Explain that it had thin walls made of animal skin. Now you want the children to convert their dugouts into coracles by simply pressing out the walls and raising them a little.
● Let the children make their coracles. They should make sure that there are not any holes in the walls and floor before they test them.

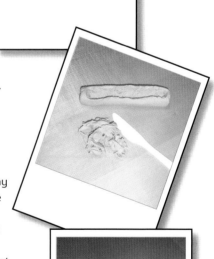

Extension
You may like to explore the idea of why some things float and others sink. Take a small empty plastic bottle, sealed, and let a child place it underwater and release it. The bottle should pop up. Explain that water pushes on things that enter it and if the object is light in weight like the bottle, it will float. Take a solid metal object and let a child place it on the water and let it go. The object sinks because its weight is stronger than the water's push. When the children were making their dugouts they were reducing the weight of their boat until it was weaker than the push of the water.

Lesson 2 Submarine

AGES 7–9

Objectives
● To know how to assemble components to make a model submarine.
● To be able to control the submarine so that it submerges and rises.

Subject references
Science
● Learn that objects are pulled downwards because of the gravitational attraction between them and the Earth.
(NC: KS2 Sc4 2b)
● Learn that when objects are pushed an opposing push can be felt.
(NC: KS2 Sc4 4d)
Design and technology
● Assemble, join and combine components.
(NC: KS2 2d)
● Reflect on the progress of their work and identify ways they could improve the product.
(NC: KS2 3a)

Resources and preparation
● Each child or group will need: a photocopy of page 46, a 500ml plastic bottle, with two holes cut in one side and one hole cut in the opposite side (see page 46), nine 2p coins or equivalent, sticky tape, a lump of Plasticine® and a length of plastic tubing (0.5cm internal diameter) about 80cm long, a sink or a large deep bowl of water. Note that shared objects that are put in the mouth, like the tube, should be disinfected. (See page 11 of *Be Safe! Health and Safety in Primary School Science and Technology* published by the ASE.)
● For the starter, you will need: a large deep bowl of water and a 500ml plastic bottle without holes in it and with its cap.
● You may wish to visit the teacher's resource www.pbs.org/wgbh/nova/teachers/faq.html#q03 for more information about discoveries made using the deep-sea machines, and to obtain more ideas for this lesson.

Starter
Take an empty plastic bottle with the cap closed and ask the children what will happen when you put it in the bowl of water. Look for an answer about the bottle floating. Push the bottle under the water and ask what will happen when you release

it. Look for an answer about it rising to the surface. Release the bottle and tell the children about the force called the upthrust. Ask how you could make the bottle sink, and look for an answer about filling it with water. Some children may think that the bottle will still float, so fill the bottle and explain that the combined weight of the water and the bottle overcome the upthrust and make the bottle sink. Explain that a submarine rises and sinks by varying the amount of air and water it carries in special containers called ballast tanks.

What to do
● Tell the children that they are going to make a model submarine, which is really just a ballast tank. Issue the photocopiable and go through the first three stages, using the notes below, then let the children try to make the submarine. 1) Place the submarine on its side with one hole upwards, then put a pile of three coins on the outside of the bottle between the neck and the first hole. They should then fix the coins to the bottle with a strip of sticky tape. 2) Add the second and third piles of coins between the holes. 3) Put one end of the plastic tube into the bottle until it reaches halfway down the bottle. The lump of Plasticine® should be wrapped around the tube at the neck of the

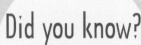

Did you know?
The bathyscape is a submarine which makes dives of 10900m to the bottom of the ocean.

IMAGE © OWNMOMENT. STOCK.XCHNG

HOTTOPICS Inventions

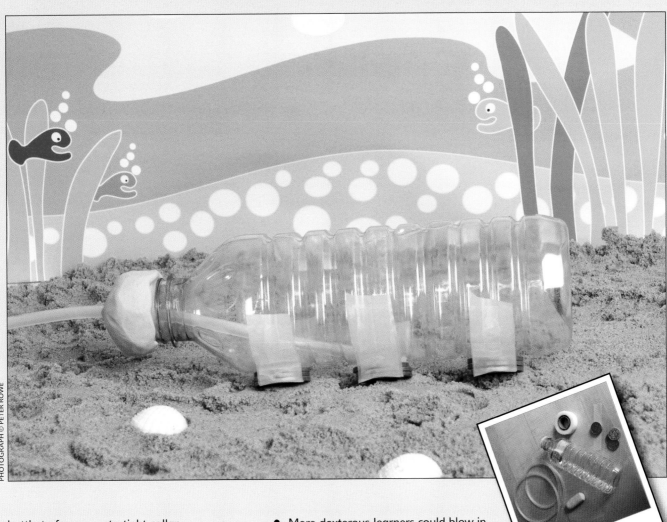

PHOTOGRAPH © PETER ROWE

bottle to form a watertight collar.
● When a submarine is ready to be launched, let the child or group put the bottle in the water. It should sink slowly. If the bottle tips up, a bubble may form at one end and prevent further sinking. If this happens, the tube can be used to manoeuvre the bottle until it is horizontal. The bubble will move under the single hole and the bottle will sink.
● The bottle can be raised by blowing down the tube. Water may shoot out of the top hole and the bottle will not completely empty as some air will escape through this hole. The idea is to show that by controlling the amount of air and water in the submarine, it sinks and rises. It is not intended to remove all the water from the bottle. Make sure that the children realise this and do not spend time trying to blow all the water out.
● Let the children submerge their submarine and then raise it again.

Differentiation
● Less dexterous learners may need help sticking the piles of coins to the bottle and making the Plasticine® collar. They can practise manoeuvring the submarine so that the bubble always forms under the hole and the submarine sinks quickly.

● More dexterous learners could blow in just enough air to make the submarine float just below the surface of the water.

Assessment
The children can be assessed on the ease with which they assemble their submarine and on how they make it sink and rise in the water.

Plenary
● Review the submarines, and discuss any problems that arose, such as the coins falling off, or the Plasticine® collar working loose if people pulled too hard on the tube. Ask the children how they might improve the submarine or design a better one. For example, they may like to make one without a hole in the top to see if all the water can be blown out. They may then find that the submarine is more difficult to fill with water.
● Discuss how the use of deep-sea vessels has led to many discoveries about the natural world.

Outcomes
● The children can assemble the components of a simple submarine.
● They can make the submarine fall and rise in water.

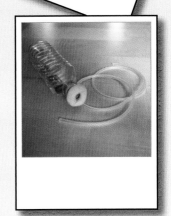

HOTTOPICS Inventions

Lesson 3 A wing and a jet

IMAGE © WEATHERBOX, STOCK.XCHNG

AGES 9–11

Objectives
- To make and test an aerofoil shape.
- To make and test a simple jet.

Subject references
Science
- Learn that objects are pulled downwards because of the gravitational attraction between them and the Earth (and the wing provides lift to oppose it).
(NC: KS2 Sc4 2b)
- Learn that when an object (the escaping gas moving backwards) is pushed there is an opposing push in the opposite direction (sending the balloon forwards).
(NC: KS2 Sc4 2d)

English
- Inform and explain, focusing on the subject matter and how to convey it in sufficient detail to the reader.
(NC: KS2 En3 9b)

Resources and preparation
- Each child or group will need:
a photocopy of page 47, scissors, string, sticky tape, a long balloon, a straw, a long piece of fine thread, hairdryer (optional), secondary sources on aircraft and their development (pictures at www.flyingmachines.org/mont.html give a sense of what it was like in the early days of aircraft, and www.keveney.com/jets.html has animations featuring jet engines).

What to do
- Tell the children that many people have tried to invent flying machines. Explain that the key to wing design is the aerofoil shape and draw an example on the board. Explain how a wing works using the information on page 40.
- Issue the photocopiable and ask the children to cut out the rectangle and make the two holes in it. Let the children thread the string through the hole as the picture shows and fold and stick the paper to make the aerofoil shape.
- The children should test their aerofoil shapes by holding them up and blowing directly at them from about 10 or 12 cm away. Make sure the children are not

blowing underneath the shape. The children may find that blowing a little to the top also produces lift. Alternatively, you could test the shapes with a hairdryer.
- Tell the children that you are now going to look at how a jet engine works. Ask them to inflate a balloon and stick a straw onto it with tape (one child will have to grip the balloon end so that it does not deflate).
- A fine thread should then be tied to a hook on the wall or a bookshelf. The other end of the thread should be inserted through the straw attached to the balloon.
- The thread should then be pulled tight, as shown in the diagram on page 47.
- Encourage the children to predict how far the balloon will travel. The balloon can then be released and their predictions tested.
- You could conclude the work on jets by looking at appropriate websites.

Extension
Children could find out about the development of aviation, or they could take one type of aircraft, such as a helicopter, propeller-driven aeroplane, jet aircraft or hot-air balloon, research how it works and write an account of what it would be like to fly it.

SCHOLASTIC
www.scholastic.co.uk

A dugout and a coracle

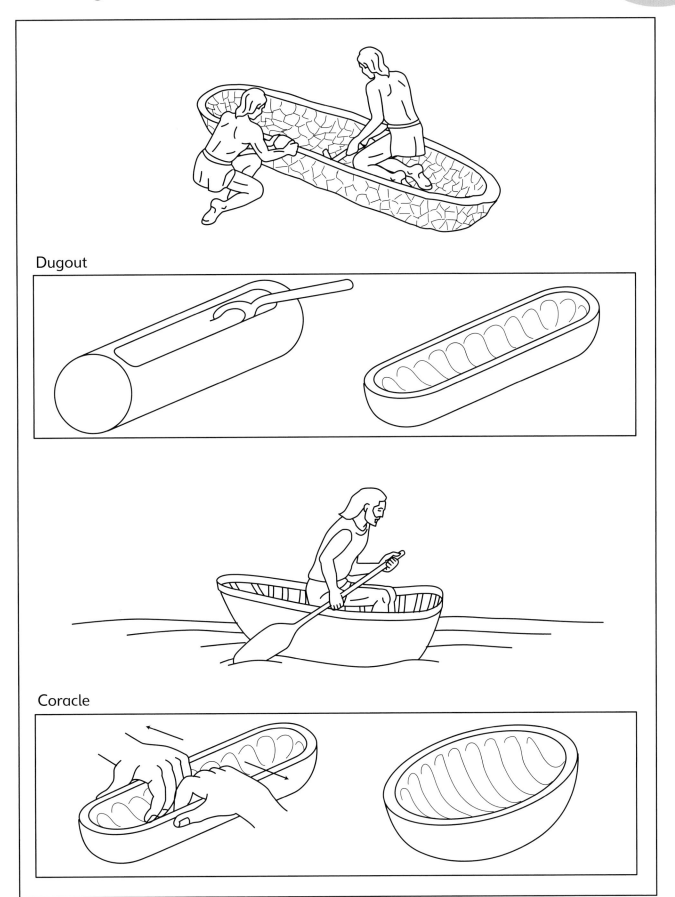

Dugout

Coracle

HOT TOPICS Inventions

SCHOLASTIC
www.scholastic.co.uk

Submarine

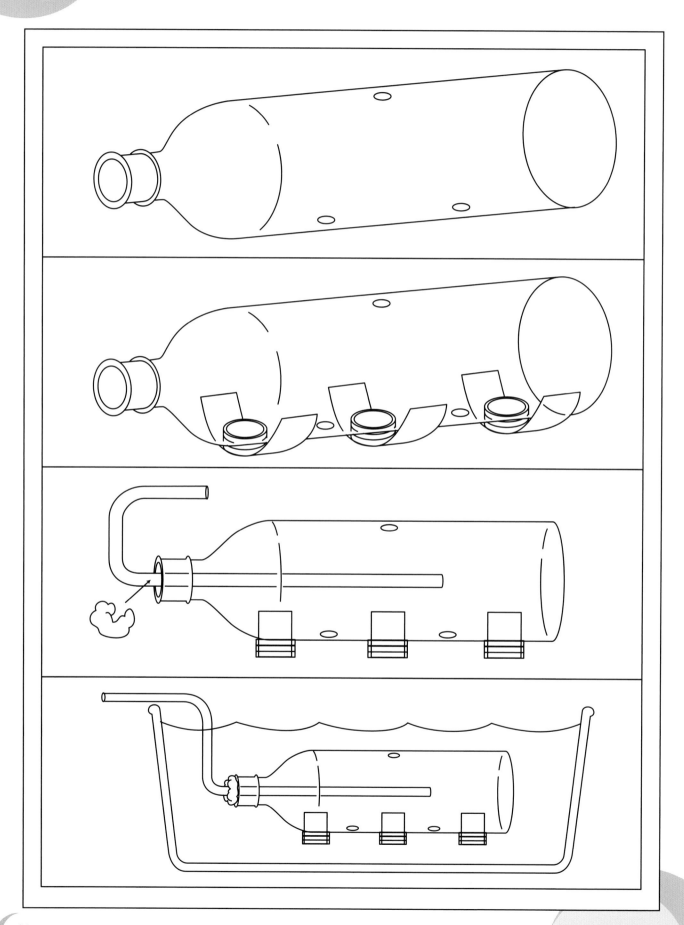

HOT TOPICS Inventions

SCHOLASTIC
www.scholastic.co.uk

A wing and a jet

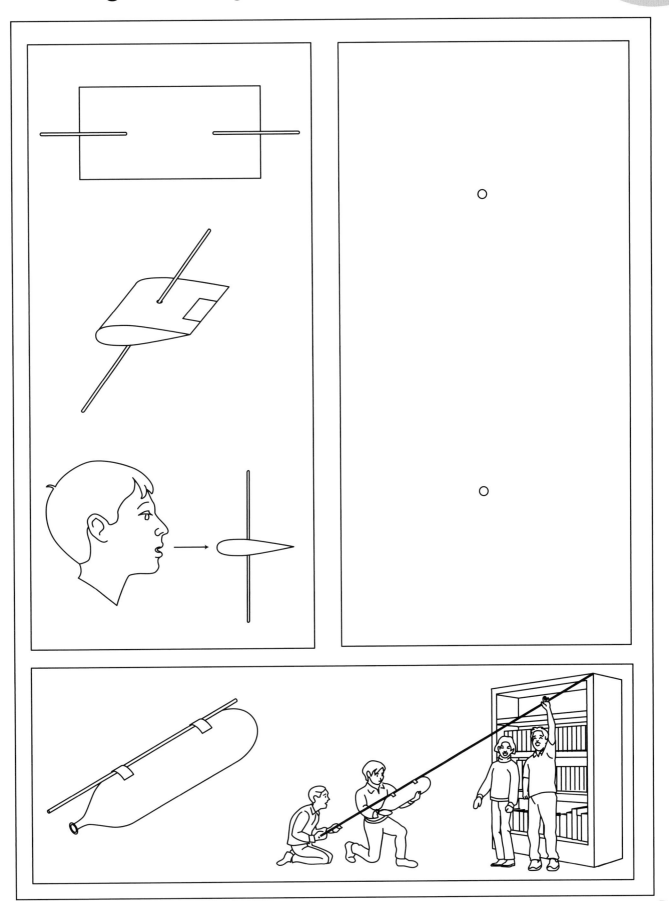

HOT TOPICS Inventions

Measuring time

BACKGROUND

Looking at the sun damages the eyes and this must be stressed to the children in any work on sun and shadows. The earliest people used the position of the sun in the sky to measure time. The day began when the sun rose over the eastern horizon and ended when it set below the western horizon. When the sun was at its highest point, it was midday. In about 3500BC, the Egyptians invented a way of using the position of the sun to measure time, without looking directly at it – a shadow stick. The stick was in fact a huge obelisk and the directions of its shadows were used to measure the passing of time, during daylight. From this invention the sundial was developed much later.

In about 3450BC the water clock was invented. Time was measured by looking at a scale, which recorded the position of the water level in the clock as water flowed out of it. In this theme, the children work with a simple water clock and a sinking water clock. The latter was used in the Roman Senate to prevent senators talking too long.

Sand timers were invented in about 700AD. Later, they were used, with a log and knotted rope, to help measure speed at sea. The log was thrown out at the back of the

boat and the number of knots that passed into the water, by the time the sand timer emptied was used to measure speed.

Mechanical clocks were invented in about 1300AD. The first one just had a bell that rang every hour. The force of gravity provided the energy for moving water and sand and, in mechanical clocks, it was used to make a pendulum swing. Today, springs are also used to store and release energy to drive clockwork mechanisms.

THE CONTENTS
Lesson 1 (Ages 5–7)
Sand timer
The children investigate how quickly sand runs though a funnel. They use two different amounts of sand and two different-sized holes.

Lesson 2 (Ages 7–9)
Water clocks
The children make a simple water clock and compare how it records time with a small hole and a large hole. They make and test a sinking water clock, and explore how it was used in the Roman Senate to time speeches.

Lesson 3 (Ages 9–11)
Shadow stick and sundial
The children make a shadow stick and mark the position of the shadows every hour.

Notes on photocopiables
Sand timer (page 53)
The sheet contains tables for recording the time taken for sand to fall: with a large amount of sand, small amount of sand and a smaller hole. A flow chart shows how to make and test a simple sand timer.

Water clocks (page 54)
This sheet shows the stages in making a simple water clock. Tables are provided for recording the time the clock takes to empty using a small and a large hole. A sinking water clock is shown together with a table for recording the time it takes to empty.

Shadow stick and sundial (page 55)
A shadow stick is shown with space around it so the position of the shadows can be drawn. A picture of a sundial is also provided.

IMAGE © GOLDDUCK, STOCK.XCHNG

HOTTOPICS Inventions

Lesson 1 Sand timer

PHOTOGRAPH © PETER ROWE

AGES 5–7

Objectives
● To make observations on the time it takes sand to fall.
● To understand it is import to repeat and compare observations.
● To make and test a simple sand timer.

Subject references
Mathematics
● Communicate using mathematical symbols. (NC: KS1 1a)
● Count reliably up to 20, extend counting. (NC: KS1 2a)
Science
● Learn the importance of making observations and measurements. (NC: KS1 Sc1 1)
● Recognise when a test is unfair. (NC: KS1 Sc1 1d)
● Follow instructions to control risks. (NC: KS1 Sc1 1e)
● Make and record measurements. (NC: KS1 Sc1 2f)
● Make comparisons and identify patterns. (NC: KS1 Sc1 2h)

Resources and preparation
● Each child or group will need: a photocopy of page 53, a funnel, a bowl of dry sand*, a spoon or scoop, two dry plastic bottles (such as 330ml water bottles) a small lump of Plasticine®, a pencil, a large stop clock (optional).
* Use silver sand from a garden centre, pet shop or a sand tray. Sieve it with a kitchen sieve and dry it in an oven for an hour, then allow to cool before use. Free-flowing table salt is sometimes recommended in older books, but be aware of the dangers of using salt. See *Be Safe!*, page 19. Put sand to about one-fifth full in one of each pair of bottles the children will use. You may wish some children to fill their own bottles.

What to do
● Take some sand from a bowl, hold it up, then let it slip through your fingers back into the bowl. Ask the children how you could find out how long it took for all the sand to return to the bowl. Look for an answer about counting, then repeat the activity and get the children to count steadily to record how long it takes for all the sand to fall.
● Tell the children that they are going to find out how long it takes for sand to fall through a funnel. Issue the photocopiable, funnel, spoon and bowl of sand for the children to try activity A.
● Stress that in science investigations, experiments are repeated, so let the children repeat the activity twice.
● Ask the children to predict what will

happen if they use less sand, then let them try activity B and compare their results with those of activity A.
● Now ask the children to place a piece of Plasticine® over half of the opening at the stem of the funnel and to predict what will happen when they put a small amount of sand in the funnel. Let them try activity C and compare their results with those of activity B.

Extension
● Tell the children about sand timers being used to measure time and show them how to make one by following activity D. 1) You may let some children fill their own bottles. 2) Make the cube of Plasticine® into a disc and push a hole in its centre with a pencil. 3) Fit the Plasticine® on the neck of the bottle containing sand. 4) Place the empty bottle on top and press it into the Plasticine®. (You may like to make the joint more secure by wrapping sticky tape around the bottle necks.) 5) Turn the bottles over carefully and check that the sand is flowing.
● Give out the bottles and let the children make a sand timer and test it. Let them try an activity such as seeing how many blocks they can line up in the time it takes for their sand timer to empty.

Lesson 2 Water clocks

AGES 7–9

Objectives
● To make observations on the time it takes water to fall.
● To make and use a simple water clock.

Subject references
Science
● Use simple equipment and materials appropriately. (NC: KS2 Sc1 2e)
● Make systematic measurements. (NC: KS2 Sc1 2f)
● Make comparisons and identify simple patterns in their measurements. (NC: KS2 Sc1 2i)

Design and technology
● Reflect on progress of their work, identifying ways they could improve their product. (NC: KS2 3a)

History
● Find out about people in Roman times. (NC: KS2 4a)

Resources and preparation

Each child or group will need: a photocopy of page 54, the top of a plastic bottle cut off about 11 or 12cm below the top of the neck and the remaining bottle bottom, a small piece of Plasticine®, a board on which to press the Plasticine®, a pencil, a felt-tipped pen, water, paper towels, jugs of water, watches or clocks that can measure in seconds, books on the Romans or any relevant previous work the children have done on Roman life.

Starter

Ask the children to imagine a dripping tap and think about how it might be used to measure time. You may get an answer about counting the drips, which helps to introduce the idea, but move them on to thinking about where the drips collect and the amount of water collected in a certain time. Tell the children that water clocks were invented thousands of years ago and were used by people like the Romans and Ancient Greeks, and today they are going back in time to make one.

What to do

● Issue the photocopiable and go through the stages in making the simple water clock.
● Let the children gather their equipment and materials (except the jugs of water) and work through stages 1 to 3. Check that they have all made a small hole through the Plasticine®.
● Ask the children, in pairs, to use jugs of water to fill the top of the clock (top of bottle), using a finger to block the hole, as stage 4 shows.
● The children should then look at their watches and note the position of the second hand as the water starts to flow into the bottom part of clock (bottom of the bottle).
● They should then mark the level of the water with a felt-tipped pen, every ten seconds, until the top part of the clock is empty. As the top part empties, the final level of water may only take five or seven seconds to settle and therefore may not be a full ten-second interval. This fraction of time should still be noted and added on to the running total, in order to find the period of time measured by the clock. This total may be about two minutes.
● The children should try the activity twice more, making two more scales, to assess the accuracy of the clock.
● Then ask them to make a larger hole and repeat the activity. They may find that the clock measures a time of only about 20 seconds!
● Tell the children that they are now

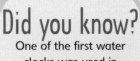

Did you know?
One of the first water clocks was used in 1400BC, in the Egyptian temple of Amen-Re.

PHOTOGRAPH © PETER ROWE

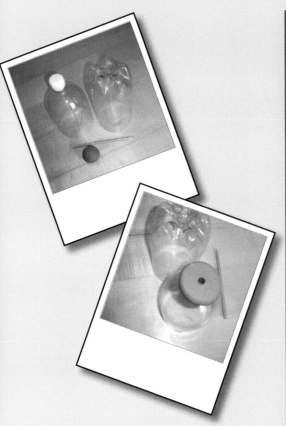

PHOTOGRAPH © KATHY WRIGHT/ALAMY

going to use the top part of their simple water clock as a sinking clock, as was used in Roman times (shown in B on the photocopiable). Explain that these clocks were used to time speeches in the Senate so that no senator could talk for too long, meaning that everyone who wanted to, got some time to speak.

● Give out the bowls of water and the information about Romans. Let groups of children work together so that one records the time for the clock to sink and one reads out the information to give the idea how the clock was used.

Differentiation

● Less dexterous learners may need help making the hole and attaching the Plasticine® to the mouth of the bottle. They may need help in reading the watch and marking the side of the bottle.
● Encourage more dexterous learners to try to make a clock with a tiny hole by blocking the large hole almost completely. If they try this, they must make sure that the Plasticine® is still attached firmly to the rim of the bottle mouth so that other holes do not develop.

Assessment

The children could be assessed on how they carry out the activity and on their views about the accuracy of the clocks they have made.

Plenary

● Ask the children to compare their results and talk about how accurate they consider their clocks to be.
● You could ask the children to predict the period of time that could be measured by all the clocks if they were set off one after the other. They should write down their predictions secretly. Ask someone to note the time when the first clock is set off and when the last clock finishes and organise the sequence in which the clocks are to be set off. Let the first clock start, and, when it has finished, the second clock, and so on until the last clock finishes and the total time is called out. The children can then compare this time with their predictions.

Outcomes

● The children can make simple water clocks.
● They can assess the accuracy of their clocks.

Lesson 3 Shadow stick and sundial

AGES 9–11

Objectives
- To observe how the direction and length of shadows change during the day.
- To relate the shadow direction to time.
- To construct, set up and test a sundial.

Subject references
Science
- Make systematic observations and measurements.
(NC: KS2 Sc1 2f)
- Learn how the position of the sun appears to change during the day, and how shadows change as this happens.
(NC: KS2 Sc4 4b)

Mathematics
- Use units of time and know the relationship between them.
(NC: KS2 Ma3 4d)

Design and technology
- Cut and shape a range of materials and join and combine components accurately.
(NC: KS2 2d)

Resources and preparation
- Each child or group will need: a compass, a plastic bottle of sand with a ruler or straight piece of wood of a similar length stuck in it, access to the playground on a sunny day (If it is sunny, aim to set up the shadow stick as early as possible in the morning), chalk, scissors, a photocopy of page 55 on card.
- This web page shows how a pendulum and escapement mechanism measure time: http://home.howstuffworks.com/clock.htm.

What to do
- If the children have recently studied the Egyptians, you may like them to make a cardboard obelisk to use instead of a shadow stick.
- Use the information on page 48 to talk about how a shadow stick was used to measure time.
- Distribute materials and let the children use the compass to find North.
- Let them set out their shadow sticks and mark the position of the first shadow. They may like to slightly chalk in where they think the shadow will be in an hour.
- The children should record the position of the shadow every hour on the playground and in the diagram on the photocopiable sheet.

Extension
- Tell the children that the sundial developed from the shadow stick. The part that casts the shadow is called the gnomon and for greatest accuracy it is set at an angle equal to the latitude of the place where it is set up. The example on the sheet, for simplicity, is set to 54°, which runs through the centre of Britain. Ask the children to cut out the base and gnomon and then fold the gnomon and stick it in position, pointing north, between the AM and PM marks, next to where the lines meet. The children then use a compass to find North and set up the sundial accordingly. They can compare the accuracy of the sundial with a mechanical or digital clock. The sundial could be used to calibrate the markings around the shadow stick.
- If you wish to talk about clocks with pendulums or springs you may like to use the website mentioned in the resources and preparation section.

ILLUSTRATION © LASZLO VERES/BEEHIVE ILLUSTRATION

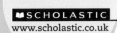
www.scholastic.co.uk

Sand timer

A. Large amount of sand

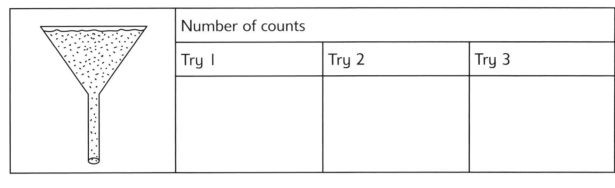

Number of counts		
Try 1	Try 2	Try 3

B. Small amount of sand

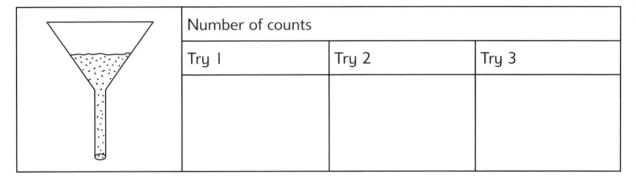

Number of counts		
Try 1	Try 2	Try 3

C. Smaller hole

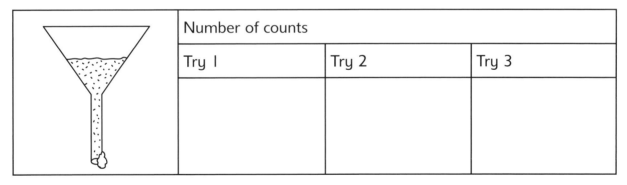

Number of counts		
Try 1	Try 2	Try 3

D. Making a sand timer

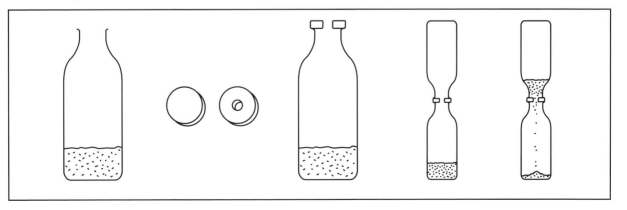

HOT TOPICS Inventions

SCHOLASTIC
www.scholastic.co.uk

Water clocks

A Simple water clock

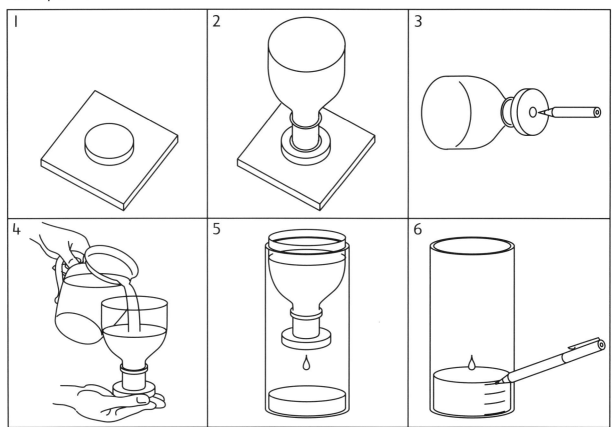

Time for small hole				Time for large hole		
Try 1	Try 2	Try 3		Try 1	Try 2	Try 3

B Sinking water clock

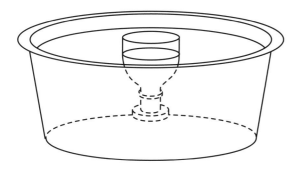

Time to sink		
Try 1	Try 2	Try 3

HOT TOPICS Inventions

SCHOLASTIC
www.scholastic.co.uk

Shadow stick and sundial

Shadow stick

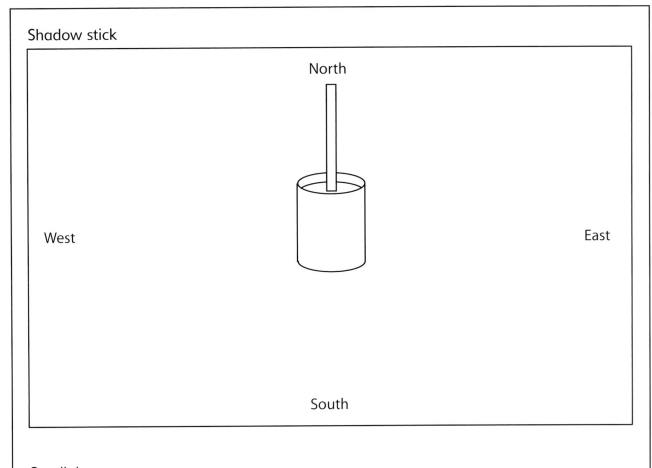

North

West

East

South

Sundial

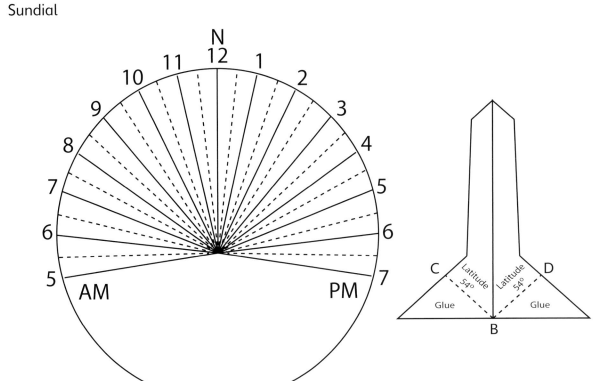

Using electricity

BACKGROUND

Alessandro Volta (1745–1827) invented the battery. It was further developed by other scientists into the form we use today. Note: the item we normally call a battery is in science called a cell. A battery is a group of cells in a line. You may feel more comfortable using the word battery for cell at this stage. Michael Faraday (1791–1867) discovered that if a wire was moved around a magnet a current of electricity could be made. From this discovery he invented the electrical generator, which is used in power stations today. Faraday also discovered that a wire carrying an electrical current has a magnetic force and when this force is combined with the force of a magnet, electric motors can be made.

Joseph Swan (1828–1914) invented the light bulb. Swan later worked with Thomas Edison (1847–1931) on improving the design of the bulb. In 1881 the House of Commons was lit by Swan's lights, followed by the British Museum. Swan's home became the first private home to have electric lights.

A modern light bulb has a coiled thread, called a filament, made of tungsten, and the bulb contains a gas called argon, which does not allow things to burn in it. Energy-saving bulbs use gases instead of a tungsten filament, which require less energy to release the same amount of light; an energy-saving bulb does not waste energy as heat, unlike a standard incandescent bulb.

People in early times lit fires on the shore to warn sailors of dangerous rocks. The Egyptians, Greeks and Romans built lighthouses that had fires on top of them. The first lighthouse in Britain to have electric lighting was at Dungeness in 1862. Lighthouses have distinctive flashing patterns; for example, Flamborough flashes four times every 15 seconds, Eddystone flashes twice every ten seconds and Wolf Rock flashes once every 15 seconds.

THE CONTENTS

Lesson 1 (Ages 5–7)
Light bulb and lighthouse

The children make a simple circuit and test it by seeing if the lamp lights. This is followed by making a circuit for a lighthouse and designing a top through which the light can shine.

Lesson 2 (Ages 7–9)
Burglar-proof box

The children make a box in which to place a simple circuit with a buzzer. They construct a switch and test it to see if the buzzer goes off every time the box is opened.

Lesson 3 (Ages 9–11)
Motor-driven fans

The children design a fan for a motor and test the current of air produced by the fan, with an air-speed detector, that they devise.

Notes on photocopiables
Light bulb and lighthouse (page 61)

The photocopiable shows the structure of a light bulb. A simple circuit drawing is provided as well as how to adapt this circuit to fit into a model lighthouse. The lighthouse picture can help the children design a top for their model.

Burglar-proof box (page 62)

This is a flow chart for the construction of a circuit and its installation in a box.

Motor-driven fans (page 63)

A flow chart for constructing a motor-driven fan is given.

IMAGE © BRAINLOC, STOCK.XCHNG

Lesson 1 Light bulb and lighthouse

Resources and preparation
● For the introduction you may need a light bulb.
● Each child or group will need: a photocopy of page 61, a battery (cell), three wires, a switch, a dim lamp (lightbulb), a cardboard roll such as the one inside a kitchen roll, sticky tape, scissors. For the lighthouse top, the children may like to use a transparent plastic cup decorated with a roof and divided into windows. They may like to make a cardboard structure to fit over the lamp.
● Visit www.trinityhouse.co.uk/interactive/gallery/index.html to see the lighthouses run by Trinity House and take a virtual tour of a lighthouse.

What to do
● Ask the children about the places in their home where a light bulb may be found. Show them a light bulb and point out its two main features – the glass dome and the filament.
● Issue the photocopiable sheet and tell the children about Joseph Swan, using the background notes on page 56 to help you. The children could cut out the picture and stick it in their books and write a few simple sentences about him.
● Give out the electrical equipment and talk through the picture of the circuit with the children, then let them make it and test it.

● Now look at the picture of the lighthouse with the children and talk a little about lighthouses, using the information on page 56.
● Distribute the cardboard tubes, sticky tape and scissors, and let the children make their lighthouses.
● You may like the children to select one of the patterns of flashes given in the background information and flash their lamps accordingly.

Extension
● Visit the website and talk to the children about designing the top of a lighthouse. Ask the children to make drawings of how they would like to make their lighthouse top, and, if appropriate, let them make it. Enlisting a team of teaching assistants may be very useful for this part of the activity.

PHOTOGRAPH © PETER ROWE

AGES 5–7

Objectives
● To know about an inventor of a light bulb.
● To assemble and test a simple circuit.
● To explore different designs for the top of a model lighthouse.

Subject references
Science
● Use simple series circuits involving a battery, wires and bulb. (NC: KS1 Sc4 1a)
● Learn how a switch can be used to break a circuit. (NC: KS1 Sc4 1c)
History
● Find out about lives of significant people. (NC: KS1 6a)
Design and technology
● A design and make assignment. (NC: KS1 5c)

HOT TOPICS Inventions

Lesson 2 Burglar-proof box

AGES 7–9

Objectives
● To know how to assemble a circuit containing a buzzer.
● To make a switch using a ball bearing.
● To learn how to install the circuit and switch in the box so the buzzer goes off when the lid is lifted.

Subject references
Science
● Construct a circuit incorporating a battery, switch and buzzer. (NC: KS2 Sc4 1a)
Design and technology
● Learn how electrical circuits, including those with simple switches, can be used to achieve results that work. (NC: KS2 4d)

Resources and preparation
Each child or group will need: a photocopy of page 62, a battery and battery holder, three wires with crocodile clips, a buzzer, a ball-bearing about 1.3cm in diameter, a cardboard box with hinged lid (minimum dimensions: 14cm long x 7cm wide x 9.9cm high), a piece of card from which to make a chute 6.5cm long and 5.5cm wide (see page 62 for the way the chute and its walls should be marked out, and decide whether to make the chutes beforehand or let the children make them during the lesson), a lump of Plasticine®, sticky tape, scissors.

Starter
Ask the children what they already know about electricity. From the discussion, focus on the use of electricity in burglar alarms. Review the children's knowledge of switches and then tell them that they are going to make a switch which closes when a ball-

bearing rolls across the contacts. Go on to explain that gravity moves the ball-bearing when the lid of a box is opened and a buzzer then goes off to give the alarm.

What to do
● Issue the photocopies of page 62. Go through Stage A slowly together, then let the children complete it before you move on to the next stage.
A) Assemble the circuit, taking particular care to connect the wire from the positive end of the battery to the red wire of the buzzer. There should another wire with a crocodile clip attached to the black wire of the buzzer. The other end of this wire should be attached to a wire coming from the negative end of the battery. At this stage you should check that the buzzer works.
B) Bind the plastic casings of the two crocodile clips together with sticky tape so that the wires are side by side and there

PHOTOGRAPH © PETER ROWE

HOT TOPICS Inventions

ILLUSTRATION © LASZLO VERES/BEEHIVE ILLUSTRATION

is a gap of about (and no more than) a centimetre between the two clips.

C) Measure and cut out the chute (if this has not been done already).

D) Fold the chute and place it around the two parallel crocodile clips.

E) Work a lump of Plasticine® around the wires behind the crocodile clip casing to provide a back wall to the chute and to give the clips extra support and prevent them from touching.

F) Roll the ball-bearing down the chute to check that it makes contact with both ends of the crocodile clips, closes the circuit and makes the buzzer sound.

G) Remove the ball-bearing from the chute, and load the circuit carefully into the box.

H) Join the chute to the underside of the box lid with sticky tape.

I) Carefully put the ball-bearing into the chute to check that it still makes contact with the tips of both crocodile clips to make the buzzer sound. Cover the end of the chute with stick tape to stop the ball-bearing from rolling out.

J) Close the lid, which should stop the buzzer. The mechanism is now ready to be tested by a burglar!

Differentiation

● Less confident learners may have difficulty with this activity, and you may choose to broaden the lesson to light and sound so that they could assemble the circuit as in Lesson 1 and make a lighthouse.

● More confident learners may wish to add an extra battery to the circuit to make the buzzer louder.

Assessment

The children can be assessed on how they make the box burglar proof. They can be assessed on measuring skills for the chute.

Plenary

Ask the children to line up their boxes, and invite a guest, perhaps the headteacher, to open them. The children can judge which box is the most effective burglar deterrent.

Outcomes

● The children assemble a circuit containing a buzzer.

● They can make a switch using a ball-bearing.

● They can install the circuit and switch in a box so that the buzzer goes off when the lid is lifted.

Did you know?

The first electric burglar alarm was invented in the USA, by Edwin Holmes, in 1858.

HOT TOPICS Inventions

Lesson 3 Motor-driven fans

AGES 9–11

Objectives
● To assemble a circuit containing a motor.
● To make a fan and attach it to the motor.
● To devise a way to compare air currents produced by fans.

Subject references
Mathematics
● Select and use appropriate equipment when solving problems involving measurement. (NC: KS2 Ma3 1c)
Science
● Make a fair test by changing one factor and observing or measuring the effect. (NC: KS2 Sc1 2d)
● Construct a circuit incorporating a battery, switch and motor. (NC: KS2 Sc4 1a)
Design and technology
● Measure, mark out, cut and shape a material and join components. (NC: KS2 2d)
● Reflect on the progress of their work, identifying ways in which they could improve their products. (NC: KS2 3a)

Resources and preparation
Each child or group will need: a photocopy of page 63, a battery, a motor, a switch, three pieces of wire, a lump of Plasticine®, a sheet of card, a sheet of tissue paper, a pair of compasses, a protractor, a ruler, sticky tape, scissors.

What to do
● Explain that electricity can be used to produce movement. Say that the machine that produces movement by electricity is the electric motor.
● Issue the photocopiable and talk the children through the activity. At stage A, remind them that they will need to make the contacts between the components secure for the motor to work when the switch is closed.
● Give out the card and mathematical equipment and ask the children to make a circle 10cm in diameter using the pair of compasses (B) and divide it into six sections, using the protractor and ruler (C). Ask them to measure 1.5cm from the centre along each radius and put a mark (D).
● The children should then cut out the circle and fold down to the 1.5cm marks. A small hole should be made in the centre of the wheel and the fan blades twisted a little (E).

● Give out the electrical equipment and let the children assemble the circuit as in F. The motor should be over the edge of the table so that when the fan is attached it can turn freely.
● Tell the children to push the centre of the fan onto the drive shaft of the motor and place a piece of sticky tape across it. Then, they should close the switch and let the fan turn. Let them hold up a piece of tissue paper in front of the fan and notice how far it is bent by the air current.

Extension
The children can make a selection of fans: larger, smaller, with more than six blades, with fewer. Before each trial the children should predict whether their new fan will produce a stronger or weaker air current than the first one. Inventive children may wish to make a wind-speed-measuring device. It could incorporate the wind speed scale shown in G. The scale should be held perpendicular to the tissue paper and the children should note the height, or angle, to which the tissue paper is blown.

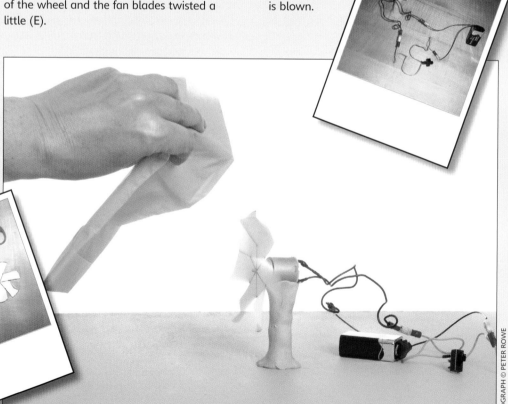

PHOTOGRAPH © PETER ROWE

HO**TOPICS** Inventions

SCHOLASTIC
www.scholastic.co.uk

Light bulb and lighthouse

HOT TOPICS Inventions

SCHOLASTIC
www.scholastic.co.uk

Burglar-proof box

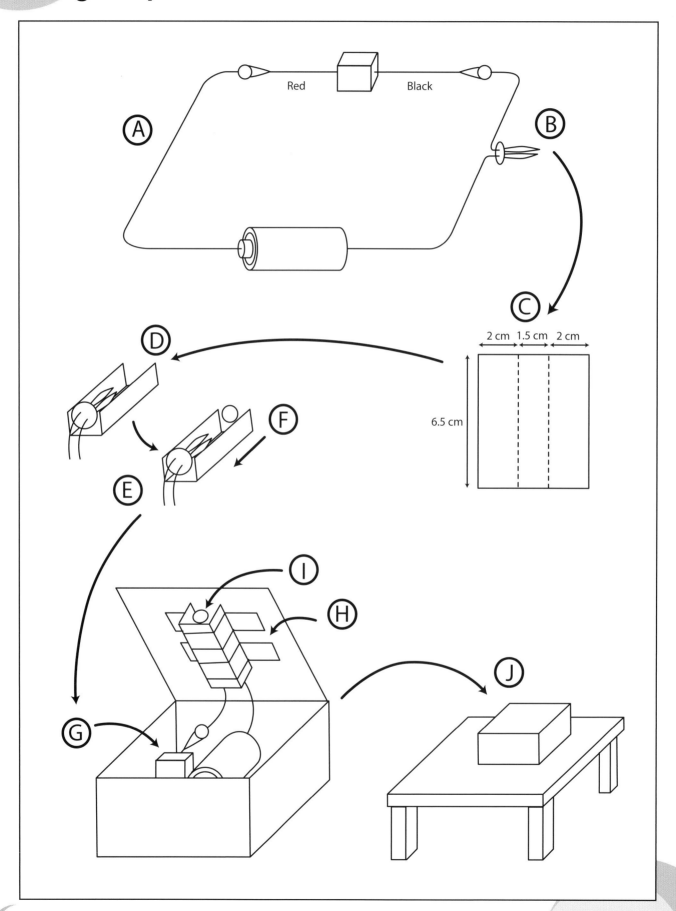

Red   Black

2 cm 1.5 cm 2 cm

6.5 cm

HOT TOPICS Inventions

Motor-driven fan

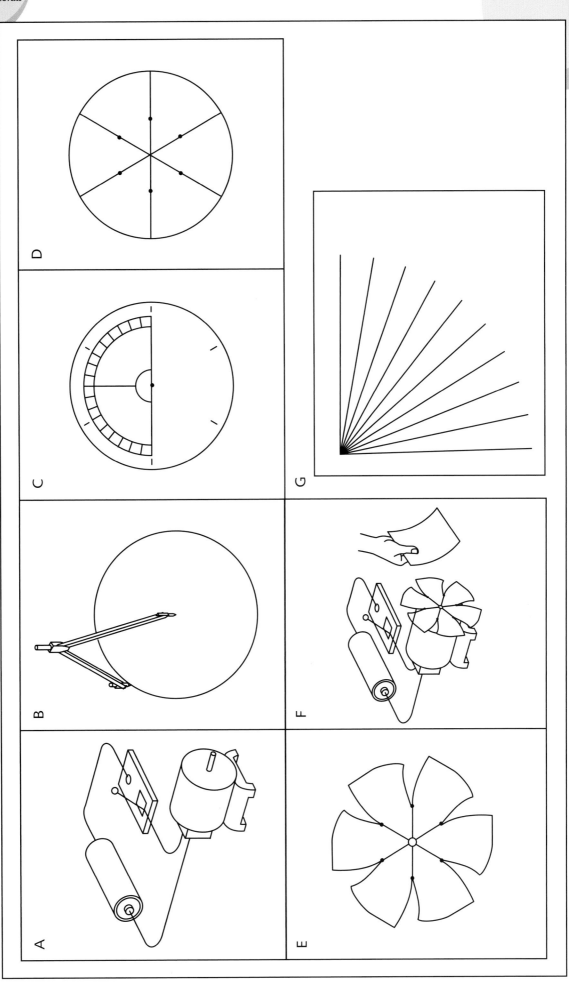

SCHOLASTIC
www.scholastic.co.uk

Communication

BACKGROUND

The information in this section follows the historical development of communication from semaphore to sign language.

The semaphore system was invented by Claude Chappe in 1791. A semaphore station had a tower with a horizontal wooden beam erected above it. On each end of the beam was a wooden blade. The blade and beam could be tilted in many directions. Each combination of tilting beam and blade stood for a letter. By changing the tilts of the beam and the blade the letters of words could be spelled out. The semaphore system was mostly used by the military. In the 1800s, it was adapted for shipping by using flags.

In 1835, Samuel Morse showed that pulses of electricity could make an electromagnet with an attachment make marks on paper. In 1838, he invented his code of dots and dashes. From Morse's work the electric telegraph was set up across the world. Alexander Graham Bell was born in Edinburgh in 1847. He studied the electric telegraph and set about finding a way of sending the voice, instead of just pulses of electricity.

Body parts and hands may have been used in a form of sign language during the Egyptians, Greek and Roman times. In the eighth century, the Northumbrian monk Bede recorded a finger alphabet. This may have been used to communicate when the monks were obeying the rule of silence in the monastery or tending the sick in the infirmary. Sign languages developed in many countries to help profoundly deaf people communicate.

Louis Braille was born in France in 1809. At the age of three he was blinded in an accident, and later entered the Royal Institute for the Young Blind in Paris. Charles Barbier, who had been working on a code that soldiers could read at night, visited the school in 1821. Braille became interested in Barbier's code and he set about inventing a better one (Braille). Braille is made up of raised dots with each letter represented by one to six dots positioned within a cell. Braille's invention was not used widely until 1868.

THE CONTENTS

IMAGE © RHEA_SUN, STOCK.XCHNG

HOT TOPICS Inventions

Lesson 1 The telephone

Resources and preparation
Each pair or group of children will need:
a photocopy of page 69, two plastic cups,
each with a hole made in the bottom, a
piece of thin string about 1m long, two
pieces of used matchstick.

What to do
● Ask the children to look at the first
picture on the sheet. Talk about Morse
code and the telegraph, using information
in the background notes on page 64 and
in Lesson 2 to help you. Tell the children
about Alexander Graham Bell as you move
them on to look at and discuss the next
illustration on the photocopiable sheet.
● Tell the children that they are going to
make a simple telephone, but that it does
not need electricity to make it work – just
a tight string. The idea is for the children
to get a sense of hearing sound in an
unfamiliar way – as Bell must have done.
● Give out the cups, string and matchsticks
and help the children to assemble their
telephones.
● Working in pairs let the children send and
receive messages and ask each partner to
write down each other's words.

Extension
● How many people have telephones
today? Ask the children to count up the
number of telephones they have in the
home (including mobile phones). Make a
class total.
● Encourage the children to ask parents
and carers about what life was like without
mobile phones.

AGES 5-7

Objectives
● To learn about
Alexander Graham Bell.
● To assemble and use a
string telephone.
● To write down the
messages they receive
and send.

Subject references
History
● Recognise why people
did things.
(NC: KS1 2b)
● Identify differences
between ways of life at
different times.
(NC: KS1 2b)
English
● The importance
of clear and neat
presentation in order
to communicate their
meaning clearly.
(NC: Ks1 En3 5h)

IMAGE © CLIX, STOCK.XCHNG

Lesson 2 Semaphore and Morse code

AGES 7–9

Objectives
• To make flags that can be easily seen from a distance.
• To use a code to send and decipher messages.

Subject references
Art and design
• Collect visual and other information to help them develop their ideas, including the use of a sketch book.
(NC: KS2 1c)
• Compare ideas in their own and others' work and say how they think and feel about them.
(NC: KS2 3a)
• Understand how colour, pattern and shape can be combined and organised for different purposes.
(NC: KS2 4a)
Science
• Construct a circuit incorporating a battery, switch, buzzer or lamp.
(NC: KS2 Sc4 1a)

Note: the semaphore activity will need more than one lesson. You may like to do just the Morse code activity.

ILLUSTRATION © LASZLO VERES/BEEHIVE ILLUSTRATION

Did you know?
The Ancient Greeks and Romans sent messages using torches and waving flags.

Resources and preparation
Each pair or group will need: sticks and coloured cloth or paper for making flags, sticky tape for holding flags to sticks, the school playground or field for testing the semaphore system, battery, three wires, switch, buzzer or lamp, a photocopy of page 70. (If you wish to use only semaphore or only Morse code, blank out the other section with a sheet of paper before you photocopy.

Starter
• Begin by raising your arms to make the children stand up. Wave at them; put your arms out in a shrug if they do not wave back; and then use your arms to signal them to sit down.
• Ask the children what you have just done, and lead them to answer indicating that you have signalled to them without speaking. Ask the children how they knew what to do and look for an answer about a general understanding of what the signals meant. Tell the children that this general understanding could be interpreted as a

code and that codes are human inventions. Tell the children that in this lesson they are going to look at sending messages using recognised systems of codes.

What to do
• Describe how a semaphore tower was used using the information on page 64.
• Go on to tell the children that the semaphore beam and blades were replaced by a person with flags when used on ships. Tell the children that the flags were usually square with a diagonal line across them. The area above the diagonal would be red and the area below yellow. In this part of the lesson, organise pairs of children and encourage them to investigate contrasting colours to see if they can find a combination that they would like to make into a flag. They could also consider different shapes of flags and different patterns.
• When the children have decided on the flags they wish to use, let them make them.
• Show the children the semaphore alphabet on the photocopiable page. Let them rehearse their flag positions in the hall and classroom. They should start in

HOT TOPICS Inventions

the 'rest' position, then work through the alphabet. When they have finished, ask them to signal the numerical sign then work through zero to nine, then signal 'J' for the letter sign and spell their name. Tell them to use the 'error' followed by the 'annul' sign if they make a mistake.

● In teams of two, the children should decide the messages they want to send, then go outside with another pair and stand a long distance away from them. One of each pair should hold up the photocopiable sheet, so that the flag person can see the code, and should quietly call out the letters and/or numbers for the flag person to send. The sending pair should check their message has been received correctly before the pairs swap roles.

● For Morse code, tell the children about how the tapping of a key attached to a wire could make an electromagnet tap out a message or mark paper at the other end of the wire. The code used for letters and numbers was invented by Samuel Morse.

● Give out the electrical equipment and let the children assemble the circuit and test it. Let the children work in pairs. One child must work out a simple message and send it in code, and the other must look at the light and decode the message.

Differentiation
● Less confident learners may find the Morse code exercise easier and could perhaps do it while other children make flags. Both groups could then share their experiences.
● More confident learners could send more complex messages either by semaphore or Morse code.

Assessment
The children can be assessed by how well they send and decode messages.

Plenary
Ask the children to share their experiences of sending the messages and compare them with making a telephone call today. Consider when and why semaphore and Morse code were/are useful.

Outcomes
● The children make flags and communicate by semaphore.
● The children make a simple circuit and communicate by Morse code.

IMAGE © MSEWING, STOCK.XCHNG

Lesson 3 Sign language and Braille

AGES 9–11

Objectives
• To understand how profoundly deaf people can communicate using sign language sign language
• To understand how Braille can help blind people to communicate.

Subject references
PSHE and citizenship
• Learn that differences and similarities between people arise from a number of factors, including disability.
(NC: KS2 4f)

Resources and preparation
Each child or group will need: a photocopy of page 71, a piece of Plasticine®, a piece of card, secondary sources on medical inventions. You could browse the website: www.rnid.org.uk for free resources about British Sign Language, including an animated fingerspelling tool and videos.

What to do
• Tell the children that many inventions have been made to improve the lives of people who have a disability. Encourage the children to talk about any they know of.
• Issue the photocopies of page 71 and use the information in the background notes on page 64 to talk about sign language and Braille.
• Give the children time to practise spelling their names using the finger spelling.
• Then let the children spell their name in Braille by assembling small lumps of Plasticine® into letters. They do not need to follow the dimensions and layout format given in the background information, but might like to use them for guidance.

Extension
• Children could try and communicate longer pieces of information using the finger spelling and Braille.
• They could use secondary sources to find out about inventions that have been developed for people with disabilities.

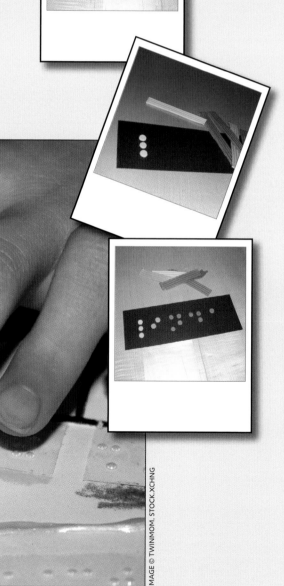

IMAGE © TWINMOM, STOCK.XCHNG

HOT TOPICS Inventions

■ SCHOLASTIC
www.scholastic.co.uk

The telephone

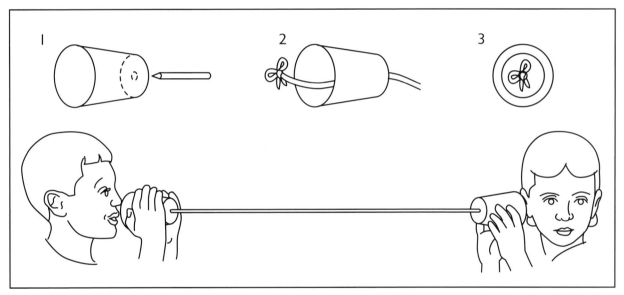

Speaker: What I said

_____

_____

_____

Listener: What I heard

_____

_____

_____

📖 S C H O L A S T I C
www.scholastic.co.uk

Semaphore and Morse code

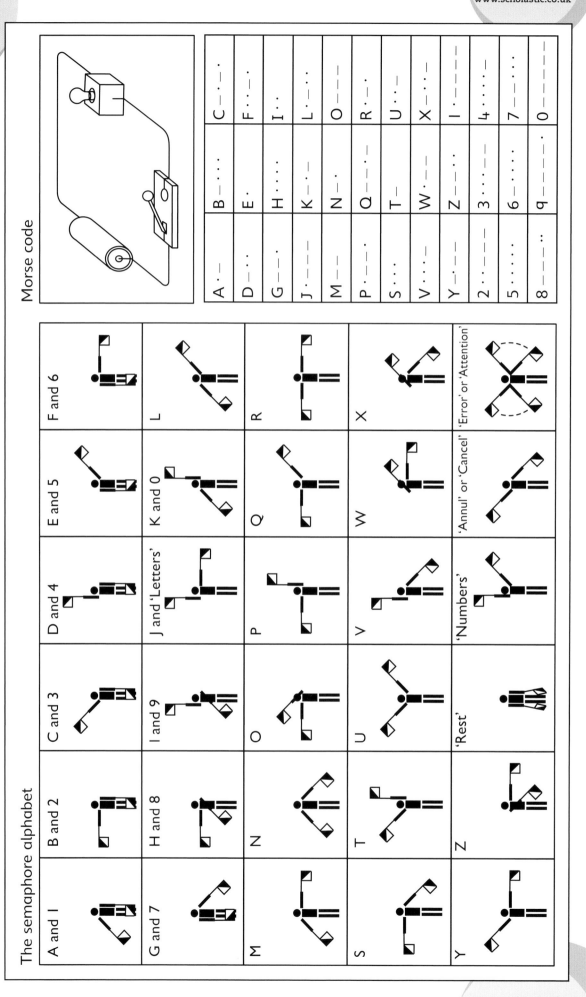

PHOTOCOPIABLE

Sign language and Braille

The two-handed alphabet

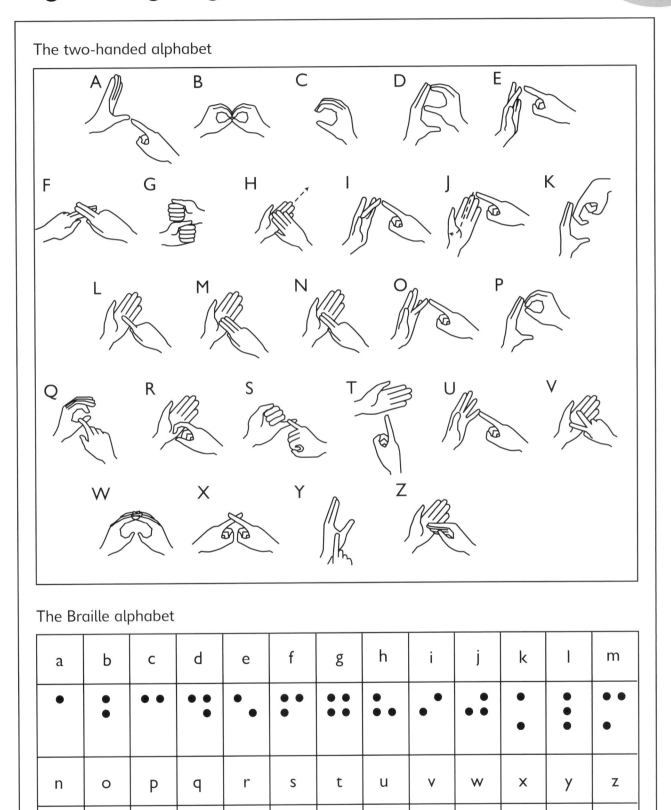

The Braille alphabet

a	b	c	d	e	f	g	h	i	j	k	l	m
•	• •	• •	• • •	• •	• • •	• • • •	• • •	• •	• • •	• • •	• • •	• • • •

n	o	p	q	r	s	t	u	v	w	x	y	z
• • • •	• • •	• • • •	• • • • •	• • • •	• • •	• • • •	• • • •	• • • •	• • • • •	• • • • •	• • • • • •	• • • • •

Inventions around us

BACKGROUND

Children have played with toys throughout human history, and dolls probably go back to Stone Age times. There are records of dolls from Ancient Greek and Roman eras. Talking dolls were invented in 1820, and Barbie in 1958. Russian children played with toy bears in the 19th century, but the teddy bear is considered by some, to have been invented in 1903. There is evidence that dominoes was played in 2540BC, while *Snakes and Ladders* was invented in 1649, and the jigsaw in 1760. Model cars were invented in late 19th-century and LEGO® was invented in 1955. The hula hoop was invented in 1958.

Percussion instruments were probably invented in the Stone Age. The horn (made from animal horn) was also a Stone Age instrument, but the trumpet, made from a sheet of metal rolled into a tube, was first made in 200BC. The piano was invented in 1710, and the music box in 1796. The first dances probably date back to the Stone Age, but ballet wasn't performed until 1581.

There are many books on inventions and dates sometimes differ. The date given might be that of the invention or when it became widely available. When children are researching dates, make sure they note which they find. Tracing the history of inventions is complicated as sometimes more than one person has worked towards the same invention, unknown to the other. Before letting children look up inventions on the internet, check the websites that you plan to use, as many do not carry the authority of a museum or similar institution.

THE CONTENTS
Lesson 1 (Ages 5–7)
Toys, music and dance
The children discuss toys and early musical instruments. They invent a percussion instrument. They look at clockwork toys and dance like mechanical toys.

Lesson 2 (Ages 7–9)
Living without inventions
The children look at a range of inventions and select five they could not do without. They consider what life would be like without one or more inventions selected by the teacher. A visitor describes life when they were growing up, without the inventions of today.

Lesson 3 (Ages 9–11)
Timeline of inventions
The children construct a timeline from just before the Victorian era to 2000. They reflect on the many inventions they use today as being Victorian in origin and compare them with some of the significant inventions made since 1930.

Notes on photocopiables
Tinker toys (page 77)
The piece of music is for piano and rhythmic accompaniment by the children, on their shakers. They do not need to see the music, as the aim is to listen carefully and maintain a strong, steady rhythm. The teacher should demonstrate the rhythm first, clapping along until it is well established.

Living without inventions (page 78)
This lists inventions that the children may use in daily life. They write about what life would be like without three inventions.

Timeline of inventions (page 79)
The main historical events are given, to be put in order on a timeline.

IMAGE © LIV2B, STOCK.XCHNG

Lesson 1 Toys, music and dance

IMAGE © LANCELOT75, STOCK.XCHNG

AGES 5–7

Objectives
● To realise that some toys were invented a long time ago.
● To invent and play a percussion instrument.
● To dance like a clockwork toy.

Subject references
Design and technology
● Develop ideas by putting together components.
(NC: KS1 1b)
● Investigate and evaluate their product.
(NC: KS1 5a)
Music
● Play untuned instruments.
(NC: KS1 1b)
● Make improvements to their work.
(NC: KS1 3b)
● Learn how music is used for particular purposes.
(NC: KS1 4d)
Physical education
● Create and perform dances using simple movement patterns.
(NC: KS1 6c)

Resources and preparation
● Each child or group will need: a selection of items that can be used as tappers and shakers (such as spoons and metal cups, tins, paper clips and other objects that can give a metallic, mechanical sound), clockwork toys.
● You will need a copy of photocopiable page 77 and someone to play the piano.
● With older children, you may like to look at this website which shows some musical inventions and gives the sound they make: www.nyphilkids.org/lab/content.html.
● When talking about moving toys for the dance you may like to look at this website to show the jerky movement of the toys: www.cabaret.co.uk/vrex/vstart.htm.

What to do
● Talk about toys with the children and tell them about the different toy inventions, using the information on page 72. Develop the discussion by talking about musical instruments.
● Say that you would like to make an instrument that you can tap, scrape or shake. Pick up a couple of items from your collection and ask the children if they could invent a musical instrument from them.
● Now let all of the children think about what kind of percussion instrument they would like to make. They could make a

simple drawing first and discuss it with you or an assistant.
● Let the children select items they need and make their instruments, then ask them to show you how they are played and the sounds they make.
● Arrange the children into groups according to instrument type, and rehearse the tune to 'Tinker toys' on the photocopiable sheet, then let the children perform it.

Extension
Show the children some clockwork toys or display the website about toys on the interactive whiteboard. Point out how they move. Play the tune to the children and let them move freely like one of the toys they have seen. A teaching assistant could film the display and play it back to the children so they can see how well they reproduce clockwork movement. The film could also be used to prompt them to improve their dance for a public performance such as on Invention Day.

IMAGE © 2007 JUPITERIMAGES CORPORATION

Lesson 2 Living without inventions

AGES 7–9

Objectives
• To consider the large number of inventions in daily use.
• To collect information and display it.
• To consider life without various inventions.

Subject references
Mathematics
• Select and use data-handling skills when solving problems in other areas of the curriculum.
(NC: KS2 Ma4 1a)
• Decide how to organise and present findings,
(NC: KS2 Ma4 1f)
• Represent and interpret discrete data using graphs and ICT where appropriate.
(NC: KS2 Ma4 2c)
English
• Inform and explain, focusing on the subject matter and how to convey it in sufficient detail for the reader.
(NC: KS2 En3 9b)

Resources and preparation
• Each child or group will need: a photocopy of page 78.
• Try to arrange for an elderly person to come into class and talk about the inventions they had when they were children and, by contrast, the inventions children use today that they did not have years ago.

Starter
Ask the children how many inventions they are wearing. They may first suggest a watch and may not think of their clothes (woven or knitted), shoes, buttons, zips and Velcro® as inventions. Tell the children that they are surrounded by inventions, from the tiles on the school roof to the bricks and concrete in the walls. Ask them to look around the class and spot some more inventions. After they have mentioned the television, whiteboard and DVD player, prompt them to consider the pen in your hand, the screws holding up the shelves, and the hinges and handles on the door. All were invented at some time.

What to do
• Issue the photocopies of page 78 and tell the children to tick the inventions that they have used this morning.
• Go through the responses as a whole class, finding out how many people have used each invention. Record the results on the board to establish the most used invention and the least used invention.
• Ask the children to list five inventions that they *could not* live without. Let them report their lists to the class, and work together to make a tally chart of the results. Ask the children to take away the collated data and make a bar graph of the results.
• Now ask the children to list five inventions that they *could* manage to live without. Again, let them report their lists to the class, and make a tally chart of the results. Tell the children to take away the data and make a bar graph of these results.
• Look at the two sets of results with the children and encourage them to comment on them. Are there any surprises? Do any inventions score highly in both lists?

Did you know?
Some of our foods such as ice cream, porridge and bread are inventions too.

ILLUSTRATION © LASZLO VERES/BEEHIVE ILLUSTRATION

HOT TOPICS Inventions

Differentiation

● Less confident learners may need some prompts in thinking about getting ready and coming to school and the inventions they might have used. They could be given one invention to consider what life would be like without.

● Challenge more confident learners to consider three inventions, which you have not already discussed, and imagine what life would be like without them.

Assessment

The children could be assessed on the way they display and interpret the data and on the quality of their imagination in considering what life would be like without certain inventions.

Plenary

If possible, invite an elderly person to talk about the inventions they used when they were the children's age. They could also talk about how people reacted to new inventions. The children could speculate on what inventions there might be in their lifetimes.

Outcomes

● The children realise that they use a large number of inventions in their daily lives.

● The children can display and interpret data.

● They realise the impact that some of the inventions have on their lives.

Lesson 3 Timeline of inventions

IMAGE © FRITZCHEN, STOCK.XCHNG

AGES 9–11

Objectives
• To construct a timeline of inventions from 1820 to 2000.
• To recognise how many Victorian inventions are still used today.
• To compare the inventions made in the 19th and 20th centuries.

Subject references
History
• A study of Victorian Britain,
(NC: KS2 11a)
• Britain since 1930.
(NC: KS2 11b)
Design and technology
• Plan what they have to do, suggesting a sequence of actions and alternatives if needed.
(NC: KS2 1c)

Resources and preparation
• Each child or group will need: a photocopy of page 79, a long strip of paper, a ruler, scissors, glue, secondary sources of information about more inventions to add to the timeline.
• For the extension, you could refer to the following website to review work on simple machines: http://edheads.org/ activities/simple-machines. The website http: //inventionatplay.org/playhouse_tinker.html. could be used to test inventive skills.

What to do
• Distribute the photocopies of page 79 and the long strips of paper that will form the timeline.
• Help the children to work out a scale for the timeline when they have looked at how the inventions group together. They may like to cut out the inventions and times listed first and see how they can be grouped, with label lines attached to the timeline, before they actually draw it. This may help them to judge an appropriate length for a clear display.
• When the timeline has been constructed and the inventions added, encourage the children to reflect on the Victorian inventions that they have used today. Ask them to compare these inventions with those of the 20th century.

• The children could go back to the timeline to mark on the births of their parents, grandparents or carers and note which inventions were made close to their births.

Extension
Encourage the children to review their work on inventions by trying the tasks on simple machines at the Edheads website, and test their inventive skill by trying the games at the Inventions Playhouse site.

HOTTOPICS Inventions

www.scholastic.co.uk

Tinker toys

Music by Sally-Anne Riley

NOTE

The left hand of the piano part has the same rhythm that the children are playing, so they should be encouraged to listen carefully to that line – difficult to do when the right hand suddenly starts playing a different, shorter rhythm!

VARIATION

The children who manage this easily could try playing the rhythm of the right hand piano part, on a wood block or another untuned percussion instrument. This should fill out the ensemble sound and emphasise the mechanical feel of the piece.

SCHOLASTIC
www.scholastic.co.uk

Living without inventions

Which inventions have you used today?

woven cloth ☐	pottery ☐	road ☐	wheeled vehicle ☐
paper ☐	printed book ☐	computer ☐	raincoat ☐
lamp ☐	soap ☐	toothbrush ☐	tap ☐
mirror ☐	button ☐	zip ☐	Velcro® ☐
shoes ☐	fork ☐	ink ☐	ballpoint pen ☐
television ☐	telephone ☐	calculator ☐	toaster ☐
sandwich ☐	compact disc ☐	radio ☐	camera ☐
fridge ☐	paper clip ☐	vacuum flask ☐	drinking straw ☐
	flushing toilet ☐	microwave oven ☐	

Which five inventions do you think you **could not** live without?

_____

_____

Which five do you think you **could** live without?

_____

_____

Write about three inventions you could live without.

Invention   Life without it

1_____   _____

                        _____

2_____   _____

                        _____

3_____   _____

                        _____

HOT TOPICS Inventions